IVA

The True Story of

TOKYO ROSE

MIKE WEEDALL

LUMINARE PRESS

WWW.LUMINAREPRESS.COM

Printed in the United States of America

Editing by Lori Stephens, Verbatim Editorial LLC

Cover and Interior Design by Claire Flint Last
Cover photo courtesy of CriticalPast

Luminare Press
442 Charnelton St.
Eugene, OR 97401
www.luminarepress.com

LCCN: 2020901732
ISBN: 978-1-64388-291-8

For Sue,
who is always my inspiration

"Don't pray for an easy life; pray for the strength to endure a difficult one."

—Bruce Lee

Prologue

IVA WATCHED THE MASTER OF CEREMONIES TAP THE MICRO-
phone to quiet down the dinner conversations so he could
begin the awards portion of the program. The dishes were
being cleared, giving her a few last minutes to settle her
nerves. She knew it would be best to go over her remarks
one final time but was unable to focus. Looking out on
the packed banquet hall from her chair at the head table,
she saw over three hundred in attendance, far more than
she expected. This was a well-to-do crowd, and everyone
she spoke with said this recognition was long overdue.

Closing her eyes, she thought back to the many years
of simply trying to survive. As she now knew, those years
taught painful but valuable lessons. She'd realized how her
youthful stubbornness and inexperience started events
rolling downhill. *If only I'd known then what I know now,
but that's the way life works. At least here I am, something
I never could have imagined.*

As the MC got control of the room, images of the people
who touched her life flew through her mind. There was her
father, Jun, now long passed, one of the few who had stood
by her through everything. Iva wondered how much guilt
drove him, since he was the one who insisted she go on the
trip where everything went wrong. *We all make mistakes,
but Dad, that was a doozy.*

An image of Filipe, now dead for seven years, flashed through her mind. Their marriage was more collateral damage for those out to get her. She regretted how he suffered in their marriage, but could she have survived without him being there? Maybe his pain was inevitable.

Other faces quickly followed one after another. Seeing these ghosts of the past, Iva remembered how people's inner values were eventually revealed. Besides being lied to and manipulated repeatedly, she now knew that much of their behavior was driven by racism and hate no matter how they denied it. Too many times, Iva heard people justify their actions by saying, "I'm doing this because I love my country."

Well, who loved the country more than me? Who experienced what I did or made the sacrifices I did all those years? If it wasn't racism and bigotry, why would no one listen and understand my circumstances? Add in the press and their need for sensationalism. What chance did a single Japanese American woman have?

Breathe. Clear your mind. Tonight is the time to say what the audience expects. It's not the forum to remind everyone of the terrible injustices I suffered or what others will likely experience in the future anytime politics trumps rationality. Tonight, this ceremony is what it is—a step in the right direction, showing that some people can listen and change their minds.

Iva heard the MC wrapping up his introduction. "And so, on behalf of the American Veterans Association, please put your hands together and welcome to the dais Iva Toguri, winner of the 2005 Edward J. Herlihy Citizenship Award."

Standing slowly, Iva gazed out at the standing ovation, wondering what the audience saw. An almost eighty-year-old woman, a bit overweight, and worn down by life. It was too rich, getting a citizenship award as someone who was not even a citizen for many years. She put that thought aside and forced herself to smile as the framed award came into her hands.

BOOK ONE

CHAPTER I
1941

L eaning on the ship's railing and staring at the lights
of Yokohama, Iva swatted at yet another mosquito.
Between these bugs and the hot, humid weather, it was
apparent she was too far from her Southern California
home for her liking. All around were countless Japanese
warships, reviving her fears of coming to a country at war.
*Stop it. I'm here, and no matter how much I resent making
this trip, I need to think of the positives. Tomorrow morning,
going ashore will be the chance to meet my mother's family,
and like my dad wrote, the next six months will create
memories for a lifetime.*

When Jun gave her a letter as her ship was about to
depart, her father made her promise not to open it until
the ship was underway. A final hug, and then she watched
her father scramble down the gangway to stand next to
her mother, now confined to a wheelchair. From the ship's
railing, Fumi looked frailer than ever, diminished by high
blood pressure and diabetes. Thinking back to her mother's
final clutching hug and haunted look, Iva regretted saying
in a frustrated tone, "I gotta go, Ma. I love you, and I'll see
you right after the next New Year. Quit worrying."

Jun's letter explained that ghosts visited Fumi in her dreams, warning her this would be the last she ever saw of her daughter. Her father was dismissive of his wife's superstitions, but his explanation helped Iva understand her mother's behavior. Despite his birth and early years in Japan, her father was almost fully Americanized while her mother clung to traditional Japanese ways.

In the letter, Jun thanked Iva for making this trip to honor Fumi's sister, who was also ill. Since neither sister could travel, the American family needed to send a representative with gifts. Iva's older brother, Fred, was busy helping their father manage the family business. What's more, he had been born in Japan. Since the United States would not allow native Japanese to become American citizens, Fred might not be admitted back into the States, given the laws discriminating against Japanese residing in America. Since Iva had been born in California, it would be safer for her to make the trip.

Remembering that she traveled without an American passport, a wave of worry ran through Iva. For complicated reasons, Iva ended up with a Certificate of Identification from the US State Department with instructions to apply for a passport at the American embassy in Tokyo. She and her father argued several times about the wisdom of this arrangement, but Jun kept saying that his daughter was only trying to come up with another reason not to make the trip.

"Dad, what about Japan being at war with China? What if war breaks out with the United States and I get stuck there?"

"You worry too much, Daughter. My native country is backward compared to the United States. Japan may rattle its saber but would never take on a powerhouse like America."

She was out of arguments and the family representative. With thirty trunks and bags that held many presents for her mother's family, tomorrow she would play the role of a generous, rich American relative. It would be fun.

"Iva, you're so smart to stay out here. The cabin is unbearable. While we were at sea and moving, it seemed okay, but now it's like an oven."

Chiyeko stood next to her, clutching her thin bathrobe about her. Iva's traveling companion was from another Japanese American family who lived close by in Los Angeles. Iva learned during the voyage how different they were. Chiyeko was clear she wanted nothing more than to get married as soon as possible and be a traditional Japanese wife, while marriage was the last thing Iva wanted even though she was twenty-five. Recently graduated from UCLA and applying to medical school, Iva aspired to be a strong, independent woman.

Smiling at her cabin mate, Iva said, "I'm getting tired and will be down soon. Unfortunately, the ship got here too late in the day for us to be processed. After nineteen days at sea, I'm ready to swim to shore."

Chiyeko laughed. "At least then we'd cool off. What are you thinking? Are you still nervous about meeting your family tomorrow?"

"Yes. Now that I'm about to meet people I will be living with for six months, it seems overwhelming. What if they don't like me, or worse yet, what if I don't like them? Me who hates Japanese food stuck with relatives that I don't know."

Chiyeko heard this complaint repeatedly during the voyage, so she gave her usual reply. "I'm sure your relatives will be kind and the visit will fly by. I think my visit will be a great adventure."

When Iva didn't respond and kept staring at the city lights, Chiyeko changed the subject. "What do you think about Yokohama now that we're here?"

Iva sighed. "In the daylight, Yokohama looked so exotic. Now in the darkness, what stands out to me is how many warships are in this harbor. I knew Japan was at war, but I've never seen so much military in one place. I hope this war doesn't impact our visits."

Chiyeko looked behind them, grabbed Iva's arm, and leaned close. "Here comes that creepy steward. I don't care how uncomfortable the cabin is. I don't want to have to talk to him."

Iva turned to look. "I'm with you. He's been chasing us since we left Long Beach. Let's try and get some sleep."

CHAPTER 2

The next morning, the two girls stumbled down the steep gangway, followed by porters with their bags. They took places in line to have their travel documents checked. After Chiyeko completed her interview and her documents were stamped, Iva stepped forward. The immigration officer spoke quick Japanese that Iva could not follow.

"English, please," she said.

The young officer, who appeared to be missing several fingers on one hand, scoffed and said in English, "American, I suppose. Passport."

"I don't have a passport. I have this from the US government, a Certificate of Identification. There wasn't enough time to get a passport, and once here, I'm to work with the embassy to secure a passport."

He scowled and perused the paperwork. Iva got the feeling he had never seen anything like this before. Already Chiyeko was gone, and Iva was feeling alone. The officer raised his head and looked her up and down.

"Purpose of trip."

"A family visit. My aunt is very sick, and I'm here to represent my family."

"How long will you visit?

"Six months. My father and mother may join me, and then we'll travel home together."

The officer raised his stamp and brought it down on Iva's documents. "No more than six months with this. If you get passport, you can seek extension. No passport, you must leave in six months." He handed the paperwork to her with a scowl.

Iva picked up her bags and headed toward the customs area. She heard the officer mutter, "Americans no friend of Japan." She pushed her shock aside and went through the door into a cavernous, noisy hall where Chiyeko pointed her out to two people who were her parents' age.

Iva's aunt, uncle, and cousins were soon beside her and started bowing. Iva had expected hugs and kisses but kept her distance and tried to copy Japanese bowing while feeling like she didn't know what she was doing. Her aunt and female cousin stood close and started to chat while the men stayed back. Chiyeko was soon there to introduce her family with more formal bowing. Uncle Hajime seemed impatient and began hustling his family and Iva along to find her bags and get them cleared through customs. Quickly turning back, Iva reached for Chiyeko, gave her a final hug, and thanked her for being such a good travel partner. Both promised to find each other in the next weeks and stay in touch during their time in Japan.

Back with her family, Iva formed her first impressions. Uncle Hajime was not very tall, but then all the Japanese around her looked smaller than the average American back home. A bit heavyset and balding, he seemed like a no-nonsense man. He grabbed her two bags and handed them to his son, Mugio. The men led the way with her uncle issuing what seemed to be a series of commands in Japanese, which she couldn't understand.

Mugio, who was about Iva's age, was a bit taller than his father and far slimmer. Iva found him attractive. In the few words he spoke, it was apparent that his English was good, and Iva felt thankful that he reminded his father to speak English to her.

Her cousin, Rinko, linked arms with Iva as they followed the men. Iva learned from Rinko's chatter in English that she was one year older than Iva. Iva admitted to Rinko that her own Japanese was limited. Rinko whispered, "My English is good. While my father speaks your language because of his business, my mother speaks hardly any English. When we are alone with her, we can talk openly." Both girls laughed as Aunt Shizu glanced their way.

Aunt Shizu was a robust woman, and Iva felt confused. Where was the terrible illness that had mandated this visit and bringing needed medicines to treat her failing health? Shorter than Iva, Shizu looked almost a twin to her mother.

When they reached the spot where the first of Iva's larger bags were stacked, Shizu stepped forward and spoke sharply to her husband. Soon the two of them were arguing. Rinko leaned close and said, "This won't be the last you see of that."

Mugio arrived with a couple of porters and wagons to transport the thirty trunks and bags. One of the porters showed Mugio some papers, and her cousin asked if Iva had already filled out a customs form. She nodded and reached into her purse for the completed documents. Mugio looked them over and showed them to the porter, who also examined them and nodded. With a rush, the rest of the mountain of baggage arrived, and the group moved on to the customs official.

Uncle Hajime and Mugio stepped up to the customs window. It became apparent that the official was angry, shaking his head and saying, "No, no." Hajime was getting more upset, and Iva watched as Mugio attempted to act as a peacemaker. The Japanese was spoken far too quickly for Iva to follow except for an occasional word. Iva could see that speaking only English at home and not studying Japanese for this trip had put her at a disadvantage.

Hajime reached back and indicated Iva should step forward. The customs official said in English, "You speak no Japanese?"

"Just a little."

"Are these all your goods?"

"Yes."

"Why do you have so many?"

"My family wanted to send gifts to the Hattoris since it's been so long between visits, and my aunt is ill, so there are medicines for her." With the mention of Shizu's illness, Iva saw Mugio look away.

"What will you sell, and what will you give as gifts? Indicate on the form what you will sell."

Iva was confused. "We will sell nothing. It's all for my family."

"All of this? Do you take me for a fool? There are too many bags for one family."

"That's the truth. My father wanted to be generous and give gifts from America."

The official scowled and shook his head. "Rich Americans showing off." With that, he waved Iva back to her aunt and Rinko. Hajime and the customs officer went back to vigorously arguing in Japanese.

Iva turned to Rinko. "Why are they arguing? Does he not believe me about this all being gifts?"

"He accepts they are gifts. Now they are arguing about money and how much duty must be paid. The duty is high, and the agent is threatening to lock it all up unless my father pays immediately."

After more back and forth, Mugio took his father by the arm and stepped back. A whispered conversation occurred and a look of exasperation from Hajime. Returning to the desk, Hajime bit his lip, pulled out his wallet, and started counting out a stack of money. With a stamp on the customs form, the official waved them on with a glare.

After a quick conversation with the porters and Hajime handing over more money, the baggage moved away. Returning to the ladies, Hajime said, "The unpleasantness is over. Now we will have a special lunch and return to celebrating our guest."

Shizu stepped forward to stand by her husband, and the parents led the way out of the hall. As the younger people followed, Iva said to Mugio, "What did you say to your father to end the argument over money back there?"

Mugio laughed. "I told him to think of this as one of his business transactions. Yes, the customs official was asking for too much money, but it was still a good deal to get all you brought rather than risk the goods being seized and perhaps disappearing in storage."

"That's my brother." Rinko chuckled. "Always practical and the one with the best chance of convincing my father of something."

They laughed and leaned together as they stepped out of the chaos of the shipping terminal and into the warm, muggy air of Yokohama.

A short walk led them to the entrance to the New Grand Hotel. In those few minutes of walking, Iva felt herself trying to cope with all that was new. On top of the oppressive humidity and swarms of mosquitos and flies, the stench of feces filled the air. They passed open sewers with human waste and its overwhelming stench. *No wonder there are so many bugs,* she thought, seeing mosquitos thick over the open trenches. Iva struggled to control her breathing to avoid gagging. It was clear she was the only one bothered, as no one on the crowded streets or her family seemed fazed.

The contrasts in building and street sizes stunned Iva. Compared to the wide boulevards of Los Angeles, the streets were narrow and twisting with no tall buildings, just shorter ones perched next to the street with no sidewalks. Many people seemed to get around on bicycles, as there were few cars in sight. Everything looked run down, and people looked poor. Most of those they passed wore Western clothes that were essentially rags, and some didn't have shoes. More than a few men wore a military uniform, often with a black cape. A few women wore traditional kimonos, some with babies strapped to their backs. Iva was pleased with those wearing Western clothes, as it didn't make her stand out so much, although her green plaid two-piece suit was in far better condition than anything she saw.

Iva was also struck by the teeming population that moved in rapid motion with no Westerners in sight. The exotic scenes she had imagined on the ship now were replaced by the reality of a poor society where people were struggling. The contrast to her American lifestyle made her thankful that her father emigrated.

It was hot. Iva could feel the perspiration gathering on her forehead as insects buzzed closely. She felt out of breath as she tried not to take in the surrounding smells. *Get to the restaurant, and hopefully it will be better there.*

CHAPTER 3

The dark lobby of the hotel was cool, and Iva drew a deep breath of the fresh air. Rinko turned to her and said, "This is a fancy place. My father would never take us here, and this is only to celebrate your arrival. The reason he agreed to eat here is that Western food is an option, so before you become fully Japanese in your eating, here is one last chance for an American-style meal."

The hotel was old. *If this is fancy, I don't want to see an average hotel. Everything is so worn. What did Rinko say? Before you become fully Japanese in your eating. That doesn't sound good.*

White rice had made Iva gag since she was a child. It was a sore point back home that separate Western meals were needed for Iva while the rest of the family ate traditional Japanese fare. One of the thirty pieces of luggage was a trunk of flour Jun had packed for his daughter so she could make bread in place of her hated rice. Iva wondered what her aunt and uncle would think of her when this came out.

As the family moved into the dining room, Iva looked around at this large restaurant. This room showed its age and past glory, making Iva wish she was back home. The restaurant was more than half full, and Iva was relieved no one turned to look at her. *It looks like I'm going to blend in. At least it's darker and cooler here, and the air doesn't stink. I need to quit being so critical.*

After they were seated at a round table, Iva heard her aunt saying something and pointing to her and her cousin. Mugio laughed and said to Iva, "My mother said you and Rinko look almost like twins. You are almost the same weight and height, and except for your pigtails, everything else is almost the same. She believes you will be good friends, and Rinko can help you translate when you go out."

Iva did see the strong resemblance. Each was a bit over five feet tall and slim with dark eyes. Touching her hair, she knew her simple hairstyle often drew comments including how young it made her look.

Rinko leaned close to her. "That will be fun. We will be like sisters."

Smiling back, she thought that having a translator would be good, but she'd need to do more herself to solve the language issue. Opening the menu, she was thankful there were English translations. She saw a hamburger with French fries listed. *If this is going to be it, as Rinko put it, better get the burger.*

After she put her menu down, she saw four faces staring at her, and the questions started about her trip, specifically how her mother was. Since the conversation was in English, there were long pauses where her uncle took the time to translate for his wife.

As she described Fumi's failing health and how frail she had seemed in her wheelchair at the dock, she saw her aunt grimace. Shizu changed the subject, and Iva next heard Mugio asking how Iva's parents had met and got to the

United States. Uncle Hajime launched into describing how Iva's father emigrated against his family's wishes because things were so difficult in Japan. Jun had been lucky to meet another Japanese American once he arrived who owned several businesses and hired him. Then Jun started his own store and had been successful.

Mugio interrupted. "Father, you know how it all happened, but let Iva tell the story, because I understand there is much discrimination against us Japanese in America. Iva, how did your father become a citizen?"

Iva watched her uncle bristle, but he said no more as everyone looked to her. "My father is not an American citizen. Nor is my older brother, Fred, who was born here. Because of the laws back home, as a native-born Japanese, my father cannot be a citizen. Instead, he became a Canadian citizen so he could travel back and forth to Japan, where he met my mother. My sisters and I were born in the States. We're American citizens."

Everyone nodded, and Mugio said, "Very clever of your father. Tell us how he met your mother."

"That's a funny story," Iva said. "After working with Mr. Kawakami for a few years, he told my dad it was time to get married, and he knew a woman who would be a good match. My father explained that he thought marrying someone the boss chose was a risk if the marriage didn't work out, so on the next trip to Japan for the business, he started looking for a bride of his choosing. A neighbor had nine daughters, and when Jun saw the youngest and prettiest, he started negotiating with her father. Marriage followed, and Fred was born."

While her uncle translated this part of her narrative, Iva saw that her aunt seemed upset. *Jeepers, I hope Hajime*

didn't translate the part about Dad picking the prettiest sister.
Of course, Shizu was one of those sisters.

Hajime paused, making Iva realize she needed to think more carefully about the words she chose. "It was several years before my father felt settled enough to bring his wife and young son to America. Since then, it's been nothing but girls, as I have two younger sisters, June and Inez. Dad's got a great store in San Diego that sells Japanese goods where I've worked during the summers. I recently graduated from college and am still studying, since I want to be a doctor."

When this statement was translated, Iva watched her aunt's face for approval but saw only disdain. It was clear Shizu did not think women should strive to be doctors.

Hajime asked, "Does your father still work with Mr. Kawakami even though he chose a different wife?"

"Oh, yes, they are still good friends. Several years ago, Mr. Kawakami got in a bit of financial trouble and asked my father for help. That summer, I drove my father twice up to Seattle to help his old boss. Those drives were fun. My dad bought me a green Chrysler Royal for school, and that car could fly. We had terrible arguments about how fast I drove, especially if there were buses in the way, but he was only playing at being mad, and afterward, we laughed and laughed. Those were special times for me with him."

Shizu had another unhappy look, so Iva figured driving was another black mark against her.

Mugio wanted to know more about her car and how long the drive was, and he seemed interested in her plans to become a doctor. Iva didn't know how much to tell them. She didn't want to say it might not be possible for her to get into an American medical school because of discrimination against the Japanese. She had been rejected even though her grades and test scores were better than some who were accepted. Iva decided to change the topic.

"Uncle, as you can see, I love to drive. Do you have a car, and might I be able to drive here in Japan?"

Hajime drew himself up. "No, I do not have an automobile, nor do many Japanese. There are fewer cars today. We must sacrifice for the war, since the military needs gasoline. You will learn to sacrifice for the emperor while you are in Japan."

The pushback to her lighthearted question threw Iva. Seeing her aunt and uncle looking at her with the same scowl she had seen on the passport clerk, she glanced around and saw Mugio and Rinko staring down at the table. *Nice start. Already on the wrong foot.*

The food arrived. As the others started in on their rice and noodles, Iva felt eyes boring in on her as she bit into her hamburger.

CHAPTER 4

Settled on the train that would take them from Yokohama to the Hattori home in a Tokyo suburb, Iva struggled with the heat, humidity, and mosquitos. No one else seemed to be bothered, and she wondered if these conditions would ever be normal for her. The dinginess and rocking of the old train, along with the smell from the toilets, were assaults on her senses. The car was crowded, and the body odor of so many passengers jammed together added to her discomfort. Feeling faint, she closed her eyes and fantasized about how a cool bath that evening would be heavenly.

The train trip was slightly over an hour. After leaving Yokohama, there was little open country before they were moving into the suburbs of Tokyo. Most of the houses they passed looked small and run down. Everywhere she looked, she was more convinced of how much poorer this country was than her home.

It was a long walk from the train station to the Hattoris' house. Iva was glad to arrive where she hoped to get some rest. Like the other houses in the neighborhood, the Hattori home was small with a sliding front door made of paper. *I wonder how this works in the rain or when the weather gets colder. It doesn't seem very secure.*

Opening the door, her uncle stepped back and indicated she should enter first. Stepping across the threshold, she took one step and heard a sharp cry from her aunt. Rinko said, "You did not take off your shoes before entering. Please come back and take them off. We don't want to walk on the tatami mats with our dirty shoes."

Apologizing, Iva stepped back outside to remove her shoes. She looked at her aunt in further apology, explaining that at her American home no one took their shoes off, but Shizu replied with a stern look.

Iva placed her shoes on the mat by the door and stepped in. Again, Aunt Shizu pointed at her shoes. Rinko bent down and turned the empty shoes so they pointed outward. "We always leave our shoes pointed outward so they will be easy to put on when we leave. It's a good habit to follow."

Jeesh, no shoes on in the house, and they have to be pointed a certain way once I take them off. What's wrong with these people?

Everyone entered, and Iva got her first look at a traditional Japanese residence. There was one main room twelve feet square and almost completely covered with mats. There was no furniture other than a low table and a single dressing table with some cushions and pillows for sitting. The ceiling was maybe six feet. Rinko pointed out sleeping mats that were piled in the corner. A small kitchen was off toward the back. Finally, the bathroom with a big wooden tub was in an enclosed porch. Like the hotel's restroom, the toilet was a hole in the floor that required squatting. Iva sighed. She knew her thighs were going to have to get used to this while hoping she might sometimes find a Western-style toilet. Sleeping with the others on one of those thin mats in this one room made her heart sink.

Her settling in was interrupted by the delivery of the mountain of luggage. The late afternoon quickly passed as the gifts were distributed. Iva knew her parents would be pleased that the Hattori family was impressed at how rich their American relatives were and that they were so generous in sharing their good fortune. The highlight for Iva was watching Rinko's excitement as she received a sewing machine. Not only would this allow her Japanese cousin to make clothes, but having a sewing machine of her own would impress the neighbors, Rinko exclaimed. Iva thought she'd never get Rinko's arms from around her neck when her cousin saw the machine.

The trunk that dampened the festivities for a moment was the one filled with flour. When Iva explained she didn't like rice and that she'd be baking bread, the whole family stared at her. After a moment, Mugio said, "We have no oven here to bake bread. Few Japanese homes have an oven, and in this neighborhood, I know of none. I don't know how you will be able to use that."

Iva felt devastated. *Bringing the flour all this way, and now being told it is useless. Why didn't my father realize Japanese homes had no ovens? So much for planning to get around the rice issue.*

While they were discussing the flour, her aunt scoffed and spoke directly to Iva, who could tell she was speaking harshly. Uncle Hajime spoke soothing words to his wife and turned to Iva. "Let me look for a place where maybe they use flour and get you some bread, but we are all surprised to learn that as a Japanese girl you do not like rice. Isn't rice served in your home in America?"

"Yes, rice is served all the time, and I don't eat it." Iva felt it best not to tell them about her separate meals back home. She did not want them to think she was spoiled.

"I think you will come to like rice while you are visiting. Here in Japan, rice is much better than in the United States. You will be happy."

Iva smiled at everyone but thought, *No, I doubt I'll be happy eating rice and constantly swatting mosquitos.*

Dinner was traditional Japanese cooking and included white rice. Eating little and fighting the cramps in her legs and back from sitting on the floor at the low dinner table, Iva was relieved to hear the offer of a bath. Rinko explained that several people would use the same bathwater because of the expense of heating the water with rationed charcoal, and as the guest, she would receive the first bath.

Entering the big wooden tub, Iva luxuriated in the water as her tired muscles started to relax. Reaching over and grabbing a nearby bar of soap, she started to lather up. In the next minute, her aunt stuck her head in to check on her and let out a scream. Rushing to the tub, she grabbed the soap from Iva and started to lecture her in Japanese.

Hearing the commotion, Rinko ran in and listened for a moment to her agitated mother. "We never use soap in the tub, Iva. The tub is for water only. Before entering the tub, you pour water over you and use soap that you rinse off. The tub is where you soak. That is the way we bathe. Now you must leave the tub so we can clean it and heat more water. My mother is upset because of the expense of using more charcoal."

Aunt Shizu stared at Iva as she got out and started to dry herself.

"I'm sorry," Iva said in Japanese.

Her aunt muttered under her breath and walked out of the room while giving instructions to Rinko.

"Rinko, I'm sorry I didn't know how to bathe and for the expense and getting your mother angry. This practice is all so new to me."

"It's okay. My mother gets upset easily. Maybe that is why she has high blood pressure. The medicines you brought, especially the insulin for her diabetes, will help her feel better. Here, put your robe on, and let me show you how to drain and clean the tub."

So Shizu did have health problems but not as bad as Iva's mother's. There was nothing limited about her aunt's quick temper, and Iva worried she'd continue to upset her. She thought back to dinner. Shizu had expressed concern about the small amount of food Iva was eating while repeatedly staring at her. With this rocky start, what would happen next?

Later in the evening, Iva helped put up the mosquito netting and took her place on a futon that Rinko told her would be hers. Unlike futons Iva was familiar with in America, which were essentially mattresses, she was given what seemed like a nice sleeping bag with a small pad. Once the lights were out and the rest of the family slept, Iva struggled to get comfortable. As the night went on, she rolled over for the umpteenth time, trying to get settled. It was still extremely warm, and sleeping on the hard floor frustrated her. On top of her discomfort, all she heard was her uncle's incessant snoring.

Iva felt more frustrated than ever about making this trip, but she knew her thinking must change, or this was going to be a miserable visit. Maybe she could contact her father and get him to agree that she didn't have to stay for the whole six months. Even if that happened, she was here for a while. She had gotten off to a bad start with Shizu, and the latest harsh looks from her aunt told Iva to be careful from now on. Where was the sick aunt who had necessitated this trip? While Shizu did suffer from some of the same conditions as Fumi, Iva thought it should be Shizu traveling to the United States, since her mother was the one bedridden. Iva fought against the resentment building inside her as she rolled over again. *I don't want to come off as a spoiled brat. Tomorrow I need to make a real effort to fit in.*

CHAPTER 5

The next morning after everyone was up, Iva did her best to ignore the noise around her and get a little more sleep. Pulling the blanket over her eyes, Iva heard her aunt speak sharply, and Rinko gently shook her shoulder. "Come on, sleepyhead. Time for us to prepare the room for breakfast."

Iva slowly brought her head out and managed a smile. "Sorry, I had so much trouble sleeping last night. I've always slept on a mattress, so adjusting to the floor with this thin futon was tough."

"As my father said, you will soon be happy. Here, let me help you up and show you how to put the futon away."

She was thankful that Rinko was pulling her up, since every muscle in Iva's body seemed to be screaming. Once up, she didn't relish squatting over the hole. Even worse, her legs now had numerous insect bites.

At the low table again with her legs bent back under her, Iva struggled to stay put rather than getting up to stretch. The food was worse this morning than she'd imagined. Breakfast was soybean soup, fermented pickles, flavored seaweed, and the dreaded rice. She picked at her food, but her stomach was starting to growl. She was going to have to start eating no matter how much she disliked the food. She thought of the bags of Hershey's Kisses she'd brought as gifts hidden at the bottom of her suitcase. It was time to keep those candies for personal use, although she'd have to ration the candy to last a long time.

"What will dinner be like? I notice what we're eating now was served last night along with some eggs. Will there be something different tonight?"

After translating for his wife, Hajime said, "This is what we will eat at almost all our meals. The eggs were a treat for your arrival. With rationing, Shizu can buy two eggs every few weeks. It is the same with meat and fish. We have some vegetables for tonight but no meat or fish." Her uncle paused. "We will make you a real Japanese, and you will soon like all of our food."

Iva nodded and smiled, but her heart sank further.

Before Hajime left for work, he suggested that Rinko show Iva the local shrine and meet some of the neighbors. That sounded good to her, as she thought walking would help loosen her muscles. Before they headed out the door, Iva snuck a moment alone in the bathroom with her suitcase, grabbed a handful of the chocolates, and slipped them into her pocket.

The cousins were soon walking the narrow and crowded streets of the Hattori neighborhood. With another warm day ahead, doors were open, and people were getting out. The smells of Japanese cooking filled the air. Iva's stomach growled in hunger even though she knew the food being cooked was far from her desired American fare. When Rinko was distracted, Iva managed to slip one of her precious chocolates into her mouth and immediately wanted another.

Her cousin introduced her to neighbors who were starting their day. While everyone was polite, Iva observed an aloofness, especially from the men. She knew that the Japanese were traditionally reserved and polite when one first met, but this felt different.

When they were alone, Iva shared her feelings and wondered if she was misreading people. Rinko was quiet for a moment. "This is a difficult time for Americans to visit, because our governments are arguing with each other. While you were traveling here, America put a block on oil shipped to Japan, so it has made life much more difficult and expensive. That is one reason you will see so few cars. There is little gasoline, and what is available must be given to the military, as my father said. Many Japanese will see you as a representative of the big country that is picking on our little country."

Iva was surprised to hear about the embargo, and now the coolness she felt made sense. She had never cared about politics at home, and she had argued with her father that Japan was at war to get out of making the trip, but now she wondered if the United States and Japan might go to war. "Do you think there could be a war between our countries?"

"I hope not, but you should ask my father. He pays more attention to government policy, especially when it affects his business."

"How many people work for your father in his tailor shop?"

"About thirty. My father is very successful. Someday I will take you to his business so you can see everyone at work."

"I'd like that. What about your brother? I didn't see him this morning."

"My brother is an interesting case. He comes and goes and is not around much since he has made my parents ashamed. Mugio is a communist, and he served nine years in jail. After high school, he received a scholarship to study in Moscow at the university. He is very smart and speaks Russian, German, and English. While he was in the Soviet Union, he became a committed communist. When he returned to Japan, he became active in the movement here, which includes opposing Japan's war with China. That opposition is illegal, so the secret police arrested him and only recently released him."

Iva stopped in her tracks and grabbed Rinko's arm. "My cousin is a communist and was in jail? He seemed so quiet and polite yesterday and didn't speak about communism, and he's much older than I thought."

"My parents will not allow him to speak of those matters because of the shame he has brought our family. You will only see him occasionally. He showed up to greet you out of politeness, since he lives with his communist friends and rarely comes home."

"Are there a lot of communists he knows? I'd love to meet them since I've only heard about communists. Could he get in trouble again with the police, and who are the secret police?"

"Hopefully Mugio will stay out of trouble, since he told me he doesn't want to go back to jail. I don't know how many communists are in his group, but I've met some of them, and they are nice people and quite interesting. My brother did tell me he liked you and hoped to see you again, so we will have to arrange a time to visit. The secret police are nothing you need to worry about or hopefully ever meet. Come on now. The shrine I want you to see is right around the corner."

The two girls started walking. *I have a communist cousin. That's the most interesting development since I got here. Thank goodness I have Rinko to help me out. Maybe I should share some of my chocolates with her.*

⁓

DINNER WAS OVER, AND CLEANING UP WAS A BUSTLE, AS Shizu had to attend an evening meeting of their neighborhood association. Rinko explained that all residents were required to be members of a neighborhood association and attend weekly meetings. At these gatherings, issues such as new regulations, allocation of ration coupons, and war bond sales were conducted. Each association reported to a regional community council, which ensured that residents were doing their part to support the government and the war. Because the men had jobs, the women did the work in the associations. Rinko's mother said it was a great honor to serve the emperor.

Iva thought for a moment. "Rinko, what you described sounds like a system for the government to control what people think and do. Do you like that?"

Rinko gave her a funny look. "No, it's not like that at all. This system is to make sure we support our government and the important war against the Chinese during these difficult times. You can see how extreme the rationing is, so we must all sacrifice and do our part to support the emperor."

Iva and her cousin had a long talk earlier that day about the rationing. Not only were eggs, meat, and fish available only every few weeks, but the Hattori household was limited to a single pint of cooking oil every three months. Things like butter, milk, coffee, and many baked goods were not available at all. Now that she understood more about rationing, Iva forced down the foods she was offered while planning on a few Hershey's Kisses before bed.

Hajime came in as Rinko was describing the neighborhood associations. "You must understand, Iva, this is a good system to make sure everyone supports the war. It is our duty and honor to make whatever sacrifices are needed. Unless everyone pulls together, the country and its honor will suffer."

Thinking that she shouldn't mention Mugio by name, Iva said, "What if the government is wrong? Don't you have a duty to speak out? What if the government is feeding you propaganda and not telling the truth? Do you think war is good for the country when people have to sacrifice so much?"

After a translation for Shizu, who had just come in, her relatives looked aghast. Her aunt threw her arms up in the air and muttered something as she fled to the kitchen. Her uncle slowly said, "The war is good for our country, since we should rule a developing country like China. We must sacrifice now for the long-term benefits. You do not understand the Japanese way, and what you said could be dangerous if others heard your words. Many people listen and report when someone speaks against the government. It is best if we do not talk about this again even inside this house. Do you understand?"

Iva didn't know what to say, but she knew this was wrong. As an American, she wouldn't put up with that kind of control, but her uncle was clear about not arguing further, so it was best to respect his wishes. She realized that she needed to visit the American embassy the next day and get her passport process going. She'd write to her father about this development of not speaking against the government. *Only my second day, and all I want to do is go home. Not so good at fitting in today, but at least Rinko enjoyed the chocolates.*

AS SHE STEPPED OUT OF THE LARGE AND IMPOSING American embassy, Iva felt good that the passport process had started. The funny-looking American staffer with eyebrows that almost extended down to his eyes took her picture, and there didn't appear to be an issue with her paperwork. The staffer indicated the processing would have to take place back in Washington, DC, and there was no timeline of how long that would take. She was told to check back in a month.

More troubling was the announcement that the United States and Great Britain had frozen all Japanese assets. In response, Japan had taken similar action against those countries. The good news was that Iva hadn't opened a bank account with the money she'd brought, so her $300 was not frozen. However, because of the asset freeze, the embassy staff told her she wouldn't be able to receive additional funds from her family. Since she'd need $250 for her return ticket, she'd have to manage her money wisely.

Iva posted a letter to her father explaining her concerns about the political climate along with an update on the family dynamics. She included the news that Shizu appeared to be in much better health than they all had thought. While she didn't specifically broach the question about returning home early, she hoped her father would read between the lines and offer that option. Then again, there was the issue of a passport.

That night, Iva joined the family around the radio for the nightly newscast before dinner. Like the broadcast the night before, the first part of the news covered events in the war with China with nothing but good news about Japanese victories. Iva wondered if the government ever put out negative news, but she knew not to ask this.

After the news, her uncle said he had a surprise for Iva: a ration card that would include bread. Iva was thrilled until Hajime explained there was an extra expense in securing the bread and that Iva would have to pay for that. "Since your family is so rich and we know you brought much money, we would like you to contribute to the cost of the extra rations while you are eating in our house. Will that be a problem?"

Out of the corner of her eye, Iva saw her aunt staring at her. Iva drew a breath as she thought about her limited funds but said, "Yes, that will be fine."

Her uncle went on. "Since you mentioned you wanted to improve your Japanese, we found a school in Tokyo that offers classes for English speakers. Rinko will take you there tomorrow to meet with the instructors. Of course, you will have to pay for those lessons and the cost to get there."

"Thank you, Uncle Hajime. I look forward to visiting the school tomorrow, and thank you for the special ration card. It's very thoughtful."

Picking up her chopsticks and taking the first bite of the hated white rice, Iva wondered how she was going to afford all this and have enough money to get home. *Maybe I'll have to skip the bread and eat the damn rice. How long before I get a reply from my father?*

CHAPTER 6

After finishing her morning session at the language school, Iva got on the streetcar. As a registered foreigner, she was on her way to her monthly check-in with the Metropolitan Police. Now in her fourth month, the police visit would be tediously bureaucratic. A lot of sitting before someone saw her, then a few perfunctory questions about her residence and how much money she had. So Japanese, she thought. All that time and effort to meet with her and nothing gained.

Iva's fluency in Japanese was improving rapidly, and she could now easily travel on her own. While the school was nothing more than a couple of rooms in an old office building, the kindly headmaster tutored her individually, saying she was his best student. While the compliment was welcome, Iva knew she still had much to learn and would need to stay committed in her studies to learn this difficult language.

Pulling her coat up more snugly against the cold, she cursed another thing to hate here. As a Southern California native, she'd never experienced cold like this and was glad she brought her best coat. The lack of central heating at the Hattori's meant the chill never left her, and often she wore her coat in the house, although the temperature didn't seem to bother anyone else. What's more, her skin was dry and cracked and itched, and her ears were red and swollen. Herbal treatments with Rinko had failed to work, so Iva had to pay for a doctor visit. The following week she went back with painful feet. "Early signs of frostbite," the doctor explained, so Iva added another layer to her clothing. Everyone said winter had come early this year and would be fierce. On top of that, she continued to lose weight, and she prayed daily that she might soon be on her way home. The treat of Hershey's Kisses was long gone, further adding to her gloom.

With no promising news from the embassy during her last visit, there was now some question in Washington about whether she was an American citizen. What's more, because of the deteriorating relations between the two countries, all requests coming through the embassy in Tokyo were closely scrutinized. She was told to be patient and check back in another month if she had not been notified. The clerk got up to leave.

Iva lost it. "Is it because I'm from a Japanese family? I was born in America, so what is this question about whether I'm a citizen? Is there some discrimination going on here?"

Iva regretted her outburst as the clerk stared at her for a moment and left the room without answering. Iva waited a few minutes, gathered her things, and headed home.

Even more troubling, she had not received a single letter from home even though she was writing several times a week. Each of her letters asked why no one was writing and what was going on there in addition to her warnings to never come to Japan. When she brought up the lack of letters to her uncle, he looked sheepish and said that since there had been no letters, it was likely that government censors were screening them and not letting any through.

Iva snapped at him. "This is the government you are so proud of and sacrificing for? They won't even let a family communicate. Is the emperor so weak that a little woman like me threatens him?"

"Never insult the emperor. You are a selfish person. I know you write bad things about Japan, so government censors should be concerned." After Hajime stomped off in anger, Iva realized her relationship with the Hattoris was at a new low.

She needed to talk to her dad. While visiting the Tokyo Central Telephone Office, Iva scheduled a Trans-Pacific telephone call for the next day. Although the expense would be significant, she needed to make it clear to her father that she had to come home right away.

CHAPTER 7

A s the streetcar trundled along the next morning, everywhere she looked Iva saw that conditions were deteriorating. Even in the middle of the day, the tram was crowded, because fewer trains were running. In a move against the British and Americans, all signs in English were removed, so Iva often had to count stops to know where to get off, since reading Japanese was still beyond her.

Out on the street, almost all cars used charcoal, resulting in far less traffic. Female Japanese police patrolled key street corners with the assignment to save chemicals for the military; if civilian women were too dressed up or wore too much makeup, the police admonished them for their extravagance. The government had recently announced the closure of all dance halls, encouraging people to stay at home and save money to buy more war bonds. In the ultimate insult to many, sake was no longer being made with rice but from sweet potatoes and acorns. Even Uncle Hajime cursed the government with this announcement.

There were a few bright spots. Iva's most pleasant memory was of a picnic in the country the month before where Rinko and Iva finally met with Mugio and his roommates. With the nicest weather since she arrived, getting out into the countryside was a wonderful diversion. There was no discussion about the benefits of communism, although Mugio and his compatriots complained that the war with China was ruining their beloved Japan. Iva concluded that communism for Mugio was not so much a strong belief but a frustration that the Japanese government never seemed to listen to its citizens. The number of resources every citizen in this small country sacrificed seemed crazy to the young men. She wondered if that would make her a communist here, but democracy in the United States was the best system she could see.

Toward the end of the outing, Mugio took Iva on a walk to show her another view of the countryside. While looking out at the vista, Iva turned to her cousin and said, "Do you mind if I ask you a sensitive question?"

Smiling, Mugio said, "More questions about communism?"

"No. It's about your mother. Why does she hate me so much?"

There was a long silence before Mugio spoke. "Promise me you won't share this with Rinko, since she is so close to our mother. Shizu resents that your father selected Fumi for marriage over her. Much to the embarrassment of my father, Shizu has been open about this resentment. Instead of my mother being a rich American, she is stuck here with a tailor for a husband. Then you show up with all of the gifts for the poor Japanese relatives, and you act so differently from a traditional Japanese. If I might be honest, she thinks you are spoiled. It's all too much for her."

Iva's eyes widened at hearing this important background. "What can I do to make your mother less angry and like me?"

Mugio slowly shook his head. "Nothing. Stay out of her way. She has always had a quick temper. Come, we should head back to the others, since it is getting late."

Iva reached for Mugio's arm to stop him. Seeing the surprised expression on his face, Iva drew back, realizing how un-Japanese her gesture was. "Mugio, sorry, but I'm not spoiled. Does your mother believe that? Do you believe that?"

Mugio looked straight at Iva. "If you say you are not spoiled, you are not spoiled, but you are very different from the women of our country. Come, we have to get back."

Jealousy. That makes sense. Poor Hajime, living with a wife who is so angry. Of course, I'm not like a traditional Japanese woman. I'm American and proud of it. Besides, what do I care what they think? The sooner I get out of here the better.

AT THE CENTRAL TELEPHONE OFFICE, A FRIENDLY female clerk confirmed her party would accept the call and pay for it. Iva sat in a small, private booth waiting to talk to her father. It would be late the night before on her father's end. At the top of the hour, her phone rang, and the operator announced the start of the call.

"Dad, can you hear me? Are you there?"

"Iva, I can hear you. There's some static. It's good to hear your voice. How are you, Daughter?"

"Why haven't you or anyone in the family written to me?"

"What? Have you not gotten any of our letters or packages? We have not gotten any letters from you. Have you written us?"

Damn, she thought. She told her father what Hajime had said about the government censors. Her father grew upset as he absorbed the news.

"Dad, it's awful here. The family is mad at me because I'm too anti-Japanese, and it's so cold I got frostbite and had to be treated by a doctor. The family is charging me for food, and my money is running out. On top of that, with relations between Japan and the United States getting worse, I'm really worried about getting stuck here."

"Calm down, Iva. It cannot be all that bad. I know you do not like Japan and the cold there, plus I'm sure the family doesn't hate you. There will be no war as we discussed before you left. Japan is too small of a country to go to war with America. Do me a favor and give your visit another chance."

Iva felt her stomach drop and her eyes fill with tears. "Dad, I'm scared. You've no idea what it's like over here. The military runs this place. Look, we can't even write to each other. I want to come home now. Please, Dad."

"Iva, you're getting hysterical. I'm sure it's not that bad. Please give it a few more days, and then maybe we can talk again. In the meantime, do you want to say hello to your brother and sisters who are here? Then I can tell you about your mother, since she missed you so much at Thanksgiving."

Iva bit her lip in frustration. "Sure, Dad. Put Fred on." She fought back her tears.

"Sis, you there? How's it going? I can tell from what Dad was saying on this end that you're not happy. Are the censors blocking our letters?"

"Yes. This place is awful. The military runs everything because of the war with China. I told Dad I'm scared because there is so much anti-American sentiment here."

"That sounds awful, but it's getting worse here also. There's discussion in the papers about a possible war, and already we can feel the anti-Japanese sentiment. Today in the store, I even had a couple of young thugs walk in and tell us to go back to Japan. It was scary, and I don't know what will happen if war does break out."

Before Iva could respond, she heard Fred arguing with their father. "She needs to hear this, Dad, and you probably shouldn't just tell her she's overreacting. I've got the phone now. Let me finish talking to her." Her father spoke, and then Fred came back on.

"All of a sudden, the expense of the call is too much, since Dad thinks I'm encouraging you. I'll talk to him after this call about you coming home soon. No matter what's going on here, you should be with us. In the meantime, let me put your sisters on so they can say a quick hello. I love you, Iva."

Iva's spirits soared. "Thanks, Fred, for talking to Dad. I love you."

There were brief conversations with June and Inez saying they missed their sister terribly. Then Jun was back, saying Fumi was resting and unable to come to the phone since it was so late. He said that Thanksgiving had been especially hard for her mother with Iva away and that he would get back to Iva soon. "I love you, Daughter. Give our love to the Hattoris."

"Love you, Dad." She sat in the booth for a long moment, feeling lonelier than ever.

CHAPTER 8

For the next several days, Iva vacillated between anger with her father and sadness. Mostly she wanted to be alone and cry. Why had Jun dismissed her concerns? Weren't there stories in the American news about growing tension between the two countries? He was treating her like a little girl, saying things couldn't be all that bad as if she was exaggerating. It was apparent he didn't want to hear about the tension with the family here. Thank goodness her brother had promised to talk to Jun, although it was scary to think about racial tensions affecting her family back home. At least Jun had said they could talk again soon, although Iva didn't know what that meant, since they hadn't set a time for another call.

When her uncle questioned her about the call with her father, Iva realized that Shizu and Hajime were disappointed that Jun had not agreed to bring his daughter home immediately. Iva knew her pro-American and anti-Japanese statements weren't sitting well with the household, and she was finding it harder to hold her tongue. Rinko had been warned by her parents to limit her time with her American cousin since she was a bad influence, so even that interaction was limited, leaving Iva feeling further isolated.

Escape from the tiny, unheated family house meant wandering the streets of Tokyo after her language classes and popping into tea houses along the way to take a break and warm up. When she allowed herself to think about her situation, she was increasingly afraid. The fear that somehow she might get stuck in Japan was never far from her thoughts.

On the first day of December, as breakfast was put on the table, there was a knock on the door. It was a messenger with a cable from her father. Wishing she was alone to read what she expected was her father encouraging her to stay and adjust, Iva saw all eyes on her as she opened the envelope.

Realize now you should leave Japan immediately. I booked passage on Tatsuta Maru departing Yokohama December 2. You have funds to pay for passage.

Iva's heart soared reading these words, but then she realized the ship was leaving the next day. The cable had been sent several days before and delivered only now. That meant it would be a rush to get ready, but she was joyous beyond description. Not considering how the others might feel, Iva broke into a broad smile and waved the cable, saying, "My father wants me home, and the ship leaves tomorrow. I have to start packing and making arrangements."

Her uncle grabbed the cable from her hand and read the message, translating rapidly for his wife. Shizu's smile told Iva that this was a good thing for everyone.

Hajime said, "Time is short if you are to leave tomorrow. We must begin immediately to get you the proper documentation. First, we must check with the American embassy about your passport. To leave Japan, you will need the approval of the Ministry of Finance. I will not go to work today so that I can help you with these tasks. Come, let's eat a quick breakfast, and we can get started."

STANDING IN THE UNHEATED LOBBY OF THE MINISTRY OF Finance with dozens of others waiting for their appointments, Iva was growing increasingly nervous. She knew Japan was a lot of hurry up and wait, but it was getting late in the afternoon, and the person reviewing her file had yet to call them in. At least things had gone well at the American embassy. Her passport still wasn't ready, but the embassy issued another Certificate of Identification that would allow her to board the ship and return to the United States.

Finally, a secretary came and said the official was ready to meet with them. In a small office, a short man in an ill-fitting, dark suit waved them into chairs. Not bothering to introduce himself, he launched right in. "This departure is not possible. We must be sure the funds brought into the country are properly accounted for. We have not had time to check with banks about any accounts and their status. Our work will take at least three days. You waited too long to bring this to us."

Her uncle started to say something, but Iva excitedly interrupted. "I've no bank accounts and only brought $300 with me. I have most of it with me and can show it to you. The money I have left will be used to pay for the ship tomorrow. What I spent was to help with food with my family and for language lessons and small expenses like transportation. It's simple."

"Simple for a pushy American to say and come in here and want immediate clearance. A full investigation is required and cannot be done by tomorrow. Give us three days to review and approve your departure." With that, the official pushed her financial disclosure form back across the desk.

Iva's eyes filled with tears as her heart sank. She could barely see the form and only partially heard her uncle starting to argue with the official. In a few minutes, the futility of Hajime's arguing was apparent as the official rose and spoke sharply to her uncle. Rising and bowing, her uncle apologized profusely, took the form, and reached for Iva's arm to leave the office.

In the lobby, Hajime turned to Iva and said, "I am sorry, but as you can see, the Japanese bureaucracy is not flexible on this issue. The cable came too late. We will have to notify your father of this development and find the next ship that we can book you on. Hopefully this will be a delay of a week or two."

Iva bit her lip and smiled as she wiped her eyes dry. She force herself to be polite, although inwardly she cursed. "Thank you, Uncle, for helping me today. I guess we'll have to start looking for the next available ship."

AS SHE FINISHED HER LANGUAGE LESSONS FOR THE DAY, Iva wondered why she was continuing to study when she would shortly head home, but she welcomed any excuse to spend time outside the Hattori home, so she attended the school. She and Hajime identified some travel options, but no ship or departure date was yet confirmed. Every day dragged as she anticipated returning home.

At lunchtime, she met in a quiet, out-of-the-way tea room with Chiyeko, whom she had not seen in a long time. Chiyeko and a friend, Yoniko Matsunaga, were excited to hear Iva was heading home. Iva was especially outspoken about her hatred of Japan and the backwardness of the country. "Besides government censors who won't let a family communicate, I couldn't even get on the ship without a full investigation. I never used a bank, but there had to be an investigation. This government doesn't care about people."

Yoniko, a beautiful young woman with hair down her back, reached across the table and strongly shushed Iva. "Be careful what you say in public. There are secret police around, and you could get in big trouble."

Iva dismissed her with a wave. "Look, I'm on my way home soon, so what do I care if I get bothered?"

Again, Chiyeko and Yoniko urged caution until Iva was on a ship and headed out to sea. Iva waved off these concerns as well, and she got up, wishing Chiyeko well for the rest of her visit and inviting her to come by in California after they both returned.

Iva went back to the language school since she had nothing else to do. As she came through the entrance, there was a commotion in the main office. She heard loud cheering and official-sounding Japanese from a radio turned way up. Sticking her head into the office, Iva saw the school employees were excited and talking loudly. The headmaster saw Iva and came over to lead her back into a classroom. Closing the door, the elderly Mr. Matsumiya looked gravely at her.

Iva asked, "What's going on? Why is everyone so excited? What was on the radio?"

"Japanese forces have won a magnificent victory destroying the entire US fleet at Pearl Harbor in Hawaii. Our countries are now at war."

Iva felt her legs give way. She had to sit down, for her worst fears had come true.

ON THE STREETCAR, IT WAS APPARENT THAT MOST JAPAnese thought their country was on its way to a significant victory over the United States. Was the destruction of the American fleet possible? Would all of the ships of the US navy have been at Pearl Harbor, and if that was the case, would an invasion of the US mainland be next? Her father had assured her that Japan was too weak to attack the United States. Clearly he was wrong.

Several young men on the streetcar were celebrating loudly, saying that they would soon join the army and help deliver even greater victories for Japan. The older woman sitting next to Iva shook her head and made small dismissive noises. Turning to her, Iva asked, "Do you not think they're right?'

"Oh, they will join the army and probably be buried on a battlefield. This war will not end well for our country."

Nodding to her fellow passenger, Iva thought, *I hope you're right.*

BACK AT THE HATTORI HOUSEHOLD, IVA FOUND THE family gathered around their old radio, including Mugio, whom she hadn't seen since the picnic. Her aunt began interrogating Iva. "What do you think of the mighty United

States now? Don't you think it's time you became a Japanese citizen so you will be on the winning side?"

Her aunt's look was smug, and her uncle didn't bother to translate, since Iva now knew enough Japanese to understand. To everyone's surprise, Iva responded in Japanese. "No, I will never be a Japanese citizen. I was born an American, and I will always be an American. Japan made a huge mistake in attacking the United States, and I will do anything I can to help them win the war."

Shizu rose and screamed at her. "Evil and ungrateful girl. You are not real family. How can you be when you don't even like our rice? Leave this house. Go find your American friends now."

Iva caught her breath as the impact of her aunt's angry words hit her. Her uncle was up, lecturing his wife. For the first time, Iva watched Hajime not try to placate Shizu. Instead, he was lecturing her that Iva was family, and she wasn't going anywhere. The war was not her fault, and the Hattori family had an obligation to take care of their niece. "Now go make dinner, woman, and keep your angry tongue silenced," he said.

Shizu glared at Iva, but she headed into the kitchen, calling to Rinko to help her. Iva quietly said, "Thank you." Her uncle waved dismissively toward his wife. Not knowing what else to say, Iva sat down and looked quietly at the floor.

Mugio spoke. "I am sorry you were not able to get on that ship last week. Hopefully there will be another ship so that you can leave."

Iva nodded. "Why are you here? It's been a long time since you visited."

"With the news about the start of the war, we all knew

the police would come looking for us. I came here to try and hide, although it's likely this will only delay my going to jail. My being here has further aggravated my mother and has not helped your cause."

Iva smiled sadly at Mugio. "I'm sorry."

"No, Iva, you are the one to feel sorry for."

CHAPTER 9

The next morning, Hajime and Iva set out for the steamship office to see what options there might be for another ship. Once there, it was apparent there would be no further ships to the United States, and the *Tatsuta Maru* had already turned around and would be returning to Japan. Maybe it was lucky she had not been able to start that voyage. The elderly clerk suggested they check with the American embassy or other embassies to see what arrangements they made to evacuate staff.

Once at the American embassy, they quickly saw that it had been sealed off by Japanese army troops and was not approachable. While heading back to the streetcar, Hajime said, "We should head home. I know the steamship clerk said other embassies might be a possibility. Give me some time to see what options I can discover through my government contacts. In the meantime, try to be as nice as you can to Shizu, and do not say Japan will lose the war. I think you are right, but there is no way to convince your aunt of that right now."

Iva stopped to embrace him. "Thank you for helping me. I know this is hard for you, but I don't know what to do. Last night I couldn't sleep, since I realize I may be stuck here for the whole war. If I cannot get to the embassy and the censors aren't letting my family's letters through, how will I hear from them and get any help? I'm scared, Uncle."

He hugged her and then let her go. "I will do everything I can to help you, but there is only so much I can do to manage your aunt. In the meantime, let's get home and out of this cold."

Iva took the arm he offered. Her mind buzzed. *If there is only so much you can do to protect me from Shizu, what can you do if the police start coming after me as they will for Mugio?*

SHIZU WAS THERE WHEN THEY GOT BACK AND ALREADY agitated. She shouted at her husband that the police had come for Mugio, and she was glad to be rid of him. The neighbors all watched as their son was taken away, and the shame of the family was apparent. How was she supposed to hold her head up when the neighborhood association next met? She turned on Iva. Had she made arrangements to leave? Several neighbors were asking what would happen with their American niece who spoke against Japan.

Hajime closed his eyes and said it would take some time to figure out what options there were for Iva. "In the meantime, get me tea and be quiet, Wife. I need to think."

Shizu stormed off to the kitchen as Hajime sat down. Iva could see the pain on his face. Perhaps he was thinking about Mugio. Rinko came in and, standing close to Iva, said, "My mother said I could not talk to you anymore." Rinko looked regretfully at her but said no more and went slowly to the kitchen.

Her uncle's head was in his hands.

⌣﹏﹏﹏﹏⌐

THE NEXT DAY, IVA WAS STUDYING HER JAPANESE LESSONS at home when there was a visitor at the door. A middle-aged, stern-looking man in a business suit came in. The whole family stood.

"I am Mr. Fujiwara of the Foreigners Section of the Special Security Police. Where is Iva Toguri?"

Iva stepped forward. "That is me."

"I have been assigned as the officer to your case since you are a citizen of the enemy United States. No longer will you report monthly to the police. All contact about your status will now be through me." He handed Iva a card with his contact information and launched into a series of rapid-fire questions. What did she do each day? How much money did she have? Why was she attending a school in Tokyo? What did she do after classes? When she walked around after class, where did she go?

Iva answered as best she could with her uncle helping with the translation where needed. Out of the corner of her eye, she saw Shizu watching, that same smug look on her face. When the officer stopped his questions and was making notes, Iva said, "I hope to leave Japan as soon as possible and return to the United States."

Fujiwara scoffed. "You will not leave Japan. It is time for you to become a citizen of Japan."

Iva caught her breath. Not leave Japan? What did he mean? Would the security police block her travel? She blurted, "I'll never become a citizen of Japan. I'm an American, and if I cannot leave, I'll not betray my country."

The officer raised his eyebrows. "Western women can be haughty, but you will see the advantages of being loyal to Japan. You will not be allowed to travel or get ration cards for food and clothes. If you want to eat, you must be a Japanese citizen."

Behind her, Iva heard her aunt cluck in agreement.

"I'll say it again. I'm a citizen of the United States and will not betray my country. Go ahead and arrest me. I'd rather be in jail than do anything to help Japan in this war."

"You will change your mind," Fujiwara said. "No, we will not arrest you. If we put you in jail, that is one more mouth we will have to feed. Better you are on your own and trying to find food. I will be back in two days after you think about the consequences of your decision. In the meantime, you shall not travel outside this neighborhood. Do you understand?"

"I attend language school in Tokyo each day. May I travel to that?"

"For now, no. Reflect on the benefits of being a citizen and the shame that will come to this family if you do not." He bowed and left.

When she turned to the family, she saw the disgust on Shizu's face. Her uncle grabbed his coat and was out the door.

Why is this happening to me? Why did my dad force me to make this trip? These developments are so unfair. Now look at the mess I'm in. My aunt is the one who scares me. I can see it hurts Rinko to obey her mother and not talk to me anymore. That officer seemed mild in comparison, but what will happen if I cannot leave Japan or get a ration card?

⌐‿‿¬

FUJIWARA RETURNED TWO DAYS LATER AND LIKE CLOCK-
work every two days after that. He asked the same questions
and always ended with, "Have you decided to become a
Japanese citizen?"

Iva's answer was always the same. "No, I'll never betray
my country."

"You will get no ration card."

"That's fine. I'll make do."

He would bow and depart. The only bit of progress
was permission for Iva to travel to Tokyo for her language
classes. That gave her the relief of getting out of the house
and the terrible silence that ruled whenever she was at home.
Over the next weeks, she returned to her habits of walking
around Tokyo to avoid going home. It became apparent
that neither Fujiwara nor anyone else was checking closely
on her and what she was doing.

Iva was forming the impression the Special Security
Police officer was coming to admire her for her stubbornness. That morning, during his visit and after the
usual threats, Fujiwara smiled. "I've met headstrong
Americans like you before. Maybe we will have to see
which of our countries wins. In the meantime, I will
visit once a week."

One day in Tokyo, Iva managed to arrange a meeting
with Chiyeko, who was also stuck in Japan. Unlike the Hattoris, Chiyeko's family was supportive of her, even though
their American relative was also refusing to become a
Japanese citizen. Chiyeko's family promised to share what
food they had with her. The Hattoris were demanding

more money to cover Iva's food, and her portions were now smaller than those of the others.

The ladies agreed they might get together in the future, but for now, they should not meet until the secret police monitoring was better understood. As Iva hugged her fellow American goodbye, she felt empty. Losing contact with Chiyeko was another step in being cut off from support and understanding.

Walking home from the streetcar, Iva saw a gathering in the neighborhood, now a regular event. Residents celebrated whenever boys headed off to the military. Iva knew these were not spontaneous events but were required by the neighborhood association. Among those gathered were Shizu and Rinko, and it was clear they wanted to pretend they did not see their American relative. *Fine*, Iva thought as she hurried along.

One of the women in the crowd saw Iva. She yelled, "There is the traitor to our country. She works for the enemy."

Immediately the crowd focused on Iva, shaking their fists and yelling. Iva was stunned by the ugliness directed her way. A stone was thrown in her direction and followed by several more. To avoid being hit, she hurried into the Hattori house.

Her uncle sat there looking tired and worn. As she described what happened, he lowered his head. "Best to keep a low profile in the neighborhood. When you are here, stay inside, and do not show yourself."

Iva felt the air go out of her. It was apparent he would be of little help now.

IN EARLY FEBRUARY, IVA WAS AT HOME WHEN HAJIME saw a small notice in the newspaper announcing that the Swiss embassy was organizing a ship to evacuate embassy staff and trapped nationals who wished to leave. Her heart soared as he showed the clipping to her, but when he dropped the paper and walked away, she knew she would have to pursue this on her own.

The staff at the Swiss embassy, which was in an old, Western-style residential home, were friendly and supportive. A spot was reserved for her on the ship, but the US State Department had to affirm her citizenship. When she checked back with them several days later, Iva was dismayed to learn that the US State Department was still unsure of her citizenship status despite the previously issued Certificate of Identification. The Swiss expressed regret, but she could not secure passage on their ship.

With the American embassy closed, there was no way for her to get her status clarified. What could cause the United States to doubt her citizenship? This development made no sense. For the first time, Iva started to feel helpless. Here she was defying the Japanese and being loyal while the State Department couldn't even confirm her citizenship. Why was this happening to her? What had she done to deserve this?

A couple of months later, Iva discovered that the Swiss embassy was organizing one final ship out of Japan. The destination would be Portugal via India. Because the ship would not dock in America, there was no need for confirmation of US citizenship. Iva could get to Portugal and then figure out how to get home by working with the American embassy in Lisbon. The fare was $425, but with the funds she had remaining, that was not possible. Iva felt like the gods were conspiring against her.

The failure of these travel options did not help the atmosphere at the Hattoris. With her uncle withdrawn, her aunt ruled the roost, and life was hell for Iva. Realizing she was going to be in Japan for the duration, Iva knew that no matter how tight her finances, she had to move out. When she announced her decision at dinner early in June, everyone felt a lifting of tension, and for the first time in many months, Shizu smiled at her.

Iva chewed on her rice and seaweed. Despite the concerns about where she would go and how she would survive with her diminishing funds, this was the right decision. She was resigned to living in this foreign land for who knew how long. How much more alone could she be than she already was?

CHAPTER 10
1942-1943

Once settled into a room in a boardinghouse closer to Tokyo, Iva was more comfortable than at any time with the Hattoris. Her small room was simple and had only a small table and bureau, but sleeping on the floor was normal by now. There was still the awful bathroom down the hall with the terrible hole in the floor. At least two simple meals came with her rent.

It was a pleasant surprise that her landlady, Mrs. Furuya, was far more supportive and understanding of her difficult circumstances than her Japanese relatives had been. It was not unusual for Mrs. Furuya to invite Iva for tea and conversation in the evening. The elderly landlady always wore a traditional kimono and repeatedly said that if Iva needed help with anything, she should ask. Iva enjoyed that her landlady berated Mr. Fujiwara when he came to check on the American, asking him why he didn't have better things to do than harass this poor woman. Was it a coincidence that Fujiwara's visits were happening less often? Even this small positive in her bleak existence helped lighten her day.

During evening tea, Iva complained about being forced to make this trip and the awful treatment by the Hattoris.

After listening to this dialogue several times, one evening Mrs. Furuya said, "Have you asked yourself what you might have done better?"

"What do you mean? I've done nothing wrong."

Mrs. Furuya smiled and put her teacup down. "I didn't say you've done anything wrong, but since you arrived in Japan, you've made decisions and said things. You told me your uncle tried to help you, but when you fought with his wife, were you helping him? When you complain about your father, don't you think he feels guilty? Things happen in life, and they are not always pleasant. Maybe you would be happier if you thought of others and not just yourself."

Iva didn't know what to say as her landlady's words sunk in. She flashed back to Mugio's comments during their hike. *Am I selfish and self-centered? I was raised the right way. My father always told me I was special. Mrs. Furuya is so nice and wouldn't want to hurt me. I need to think about this some more and perhaps make some changes.*

Seeing her discomfort, Mrs. Furuya reached over and touched Iva's knee. "I didn't mean to be unkind, but life can be difficult at times. I know you are a good person. Here, have another cookie, since sweets are becoming harder to find."

THE OTHER RESIDENTS IN THE BOARDINGHOUSE KEPT their distance, but in general, they were polite and not critical about Iva's views on the war. She settled into a routine of attending language school on weekday mornings, wandering Tokyo, studying in her room during the afternoons, and hoping to be invited for tea in the evenings.

Soon there was another challenge. Along with many other city residents, Iva had taken to traveling by train into the country on weekends to look for food. Even though almost everyone had ration cards, it was apparent that what the government was distributing was inadequate. Now the poor country cousins that most urban residents looked down upon were richer, since they had food. Black market transactions in the country were easier to find than in Tokyo. Iva had to walk ten to fifteen miles from farm to farm once she left the train, and she usually found a farmer with extra sweet potatoes or a sympathetic heart. A male traveler on a Saturday morning train told Iva she had an advantage in making deals, as she was a single woman dressed like a teenager. If she wanted to do even better, she should bring a child with her, as that often moved the sympathies of a farmer's wife.

Remembering the words of her landlady, Iva often gave what she found to Mrs. Furuya to put on the table for all the boarders. This cost added to her expenses as she watched her meager funds dwindle. She used the last of the yarn that was intended for the Hattoris to knit socks and hats to sell. She could see how desperate the Japanese were for these basic items, given her minimal knitting abilities. She negotiated a reduced fee at the language school by offering piano lessons to the headmaster's children. Once word spread, several concubines who were supported by businessmen in the neighborhood brought their children for lessons. While the earnings were small, every bit was critical. It was clear to her, early in the new year, that her money would all be gone, so it was time to get a job. While her Japanese continued to improve, would it be good enough for most employers?

One day when Iva was leaving the boardinghouse, she met a young student who was new to the residence. While chatting on their way to the streetcar, Iva mentioned her desire for a job. The girl knew of an agency that was looking for people with strong English skills, and a friend worked there. She promised to ask if jobs might still be available. Later that day, Iva's new acquaintance told her that the company, Domei, would like to meet with her the next day.

For her morning appointment, Iva put on her green plaid suit, the only thing she had that was close to business attire. After arriving early, Iva had to wait, which fed her anxiety. Until this time, she'd only worked in the family store, so there was no need for an interview. *What might they ask me, and what would be the best answers? As an American, might I be sent away as someone from the enemy? The need is for someone who knows English, but will my Japanese be acceptable? I still can't read many Japanese characters. Will that be a problem?*

Another concern was that this was day two of her period, and last month she had used the last of the sanitary pads she brought. Now she was forced to use rags that she had to launder. Worrying about her hygiene, she didn't notice a tired-looking man standing in front of her.

"I am Mr. Gadow. Are you here for the job interview? If so, please follow me."

In his crowded office, Gadow pulled out a chair for her and seated himself behind his desk. "I see you are American. Tell me, how did you come to be here? Are you trapped because of the war?"

Holding her breath, Iva wondered how to begin. While explaining her circumstances, Iva found herself in a relaxed conversation with this kind man. They talked about a variety of topics and did not touch the sensitive topic of the war. After discussing her family and Gadow describing his, Iva heard the question she'd been dreading. "What is your relationship with the police, how often must you report to them, and do you have any outstanding charges against you?" He seemed reassured by her answers. "When can you start? We are short of qualified people."

Without missing a beat, Iva said, "Immediately. My budget is tight, so the sooner the better."

The rest of their conversation was about the job and what would be required. Gadow was pleased Iva could start the next day. After leaving the Domei office, standing alone in a hallway, Iva threw her arms in the air. *I did it! My first job interview, and I got the job. Not bad for a single woman having to figure it out on my own. Maybe I'm going to be okay here after all.*

Her feet barely touching the ground, Iva hurried home to tell her landlady the good news and thank the boarder for her help. *When I get my first paycheck, I'll buy her a thank-you gift.*

The next day, she met with Mr. Gadow and two others who were monitoring foreign language news shortwave radio broadcasts. The Japanese government wanted to know how other countries were reporting war news as well as domestic developments in those countries that might be of interest. By the end of the week, Iva started reporting to work at nine o'clock in the evening.

Her job was to monitor broadcasts from the United States, Australia, and Great Britain using a set of headphones. The challenge was to concentrate because of the weak signals and static-filled transmissions that left her drained and often with a headache. After her assigned broadcasts were over, she transcribed the news in English. Her inability to write Japanese was not an issue, as the army officers who reviewed the transcripts understood English. While the pay was not great, her weekly earnings paid her rent and a bit more, so she could breathe a small sigh of relief.

Another benefit of this job was learning what was going on in the war, not the propaganda put out by the government. While Japan claimed victory after victory, it was apparent that following the bombing of Pearl Harbor, the tide in the war was turning. Battles where the Japanese were defeated were not reported in Japan. Iva learned the truth as she monitored the shortwave radio. Her knowledge that the Americans were starting to push back on the battlefield made her more determined than ever to not cooperate with the Japanese authorities no matter what they might threaten.

On the job, Iva discovered the United States had interned all Japanese Americans for the duration of the war. At first, she thought this could not possibly be true and checked with the Japanese Red Cross. Once they confirmed it, Iva struggled to comprehend how this could happen. How could her country do such a thing? She remembered the discrimination she experienced growing up, including her failure to get into medical school. Now her family was imprisoned along with other Japanese Americans under who knew what conditions. It gave Fujiwara another argument to taunt her with during his visits. "How can you be loyal to a country that throws your family in prison?"

I wonder what the conditions might be for my family. I sure won't be getting any help from my father now, but more importantly, what about my mother and her health? I hope they have good medical facilities and the medicines she needs. I wish when Fumi was holding me so tight when I left that I didn't dismiss her and her dreams, just telling her not to worry. Look what happened. Her dreams came true.

These thoughts constantly occupied her mind. Pressure increased when a colleague of Fujiwara showed up one day and insisted that she accompany him to lunch. Although she welcomed the free meal, Iva was suspicious of this new policeman, wondering if he might proposition her. She discovered it was not sex this weaselly man in a cheap suit wanted. He was there to recruit her to spy on her coworkers. When she refused, he lost his temper and started lecturing her in a loud voice that had everyone in the restaurant looking at them. Keeping quiet while he threatened her, Iva managed to gulp down her food before walking out.

That was scary. I wonder if there will be follow-up and if that creep was serious about throwing me in jail or getting me fired. This government has no shame and justifies everything in the name of the emperor. Trying to trade food for spying shows how desperate they are. Now that things are settled and I have a decent job, this has to happen. I'm not going to cry in public, but when I get back to my room...

Though worried, over the next few days, Iva started to relax when it was apparent there would not be any follow-up by the policeman. After a week passed, she decided she was in the clear and counted her blessings.

A month into her new job, Iva noticed another new employee. She found herself drawn to the slim man with a gentle, handsome face. Iva went right up to him and introduced herself. Despite knowing this forwardness was not typical Japanese behavior, Iva continued her rapid-fire questions to get his full background.

Filipe D'Aquino's father was a Portuguese citizen who came to Japan to work in an automobile plant and then married a Japanese woman. The couple lived in Yokohama, where Filipe was born and educated in English at a missionary school and then a Catholic college. He was five years younger than Iva and slightly taller. Filipe and his mother had recently moved to Tokyo, leaving his father in Yokohama.

Iva and Filipe were soon spending time together. His soft-spoken manner and easygoing personality appealed to her. As a citizen of Portugal, Filipe openly shared his opposition to the Japanese war effort and his support for the United States. This made him a supporter at work where Iva continued to be outspoken in her support for the Allies. Sometimes this resulted in shouting matches breaking out, as everyone else in the office argued against Iva and Filipe. While Filipe stood by Iva when these conflicts arose, he encouraged her to keep a lower profile. "If someone at Domei complained to the secret police, we might find ourselves without a job or in jail."

Iva nodded and agreed he was right but always lost her temper when someone again spoke against the United States. Most importantly for Iva, she finally had a confidant with whom she could speak freely and share her hopes and fears. Better yet, Filipe was fascinated by Iva's native country and loved to hear her stories about America. Soon they were fantasizing about traveling together around the world once the war was over.

Back in the States, Iva had limited experience with dating, always with young Japanese American boys whom she never found appealing. Looking in the mirror, she had concluded she was too thin and looked like a teenager. What man would want her? Now she was excited that this handsome, smart man wanted to spend time with her. Still, the worry that her unattractiveness would cause Filipe to one day find someone else was never far from her mind. For now, Filipe's company was the highlight of her life, and the depression she had struggled with lifted.

One Sunday evening, Filipe invited Iva for dinner at his mother's house. Maria was a petite, attractive woman with warm, dark eyes and a quick smile. Her small, traditional Japanese home was immaculate, and Iva felt it reflected her personality. Filipe often spoke about how hardworking his mother was and how she had been strict, raising him mostly alone. His father, Jose, occasionally showed up to spend time with his wife and son but preferred to live by himself. When Iva asked if Filipe was upset about how little he saw his father, he shook his head. "If he doesn't want to be with us and would rather live with his brother in Yokohama, that's fine with me. That way my mother and I can focus on taking care of ourselves."

Maria was enthusiastic about meeting Iva and wanted to know all about the American and her family. She fussed all evening over her guest, and Iva enjoyed more food than she had seen in quite a while. It was clear Maria was sacrificing her rations to create this special evening, so Iva felt a twinge of guilt but still enjoyed the dinner. When the couple was getting ready to leave, Maria kissed her on the cheek and made Iva promise to visit again soon.

Sitting with Filipe on the streetcar, Iva felt her attraction to this man in every part of her being. Maybe it was the sake or the knowledge that he wanted her to meet his mother. She questioned whether her loneliness was driving her to care so much, or could it be love? Filipe was very reserved, and the two had yet to kiss. Looking around the car and seeing for once only a few other people, she reached over, pulled his face to hers, and delivered a big kiss. Surprised, he pulled away but smiled and leaned back to her with a long kiss. No words followed as Iva leaned close and the two held hands. *I guess I have a boyfriend.*

CHAPTER III

When early summer arrived, Iva was hospitalized because of malnutrition. As she was lying in a hospital bed in a crowded ward, Filipe sat on the edge of her bed, holding her hand. "Iva, you've got to eat more, and we have to find a way to get more fruit and vegetables. When you get food, you too often share it with your landlady and other tenants. Sometimes you must put yourself first."

Iva took in his words and didn't say anything. *That's easy enough for Fil to say, but with me working evenings and food getting more expensive, how can I do that? We travel every weekend to the country searching for food, but more people are doing the same. Not only are there more people to compete with, but the farmers have less to sell. Even the rice I hate is gone, replaced by rice porridge that's even worse. When am I supposed to get any rest, never mind eat more when things are so bad?*

Looking at Filipe and wanting to reassure him, she said, "I know I need to do better, but it's all so hard. The doctor said I'll get the vitamins I need here to get rid of the beriberi and scurvy. Somehow I'll have to figure out how to do better in the future. Thanks for caring so much."

At that moment, the doctor came in. "Filipe, good to see you. How is our star patient today?"

"Just as difficult as ever, Doctor."

Iva smiled, knowing how lucky she was to have found Dr. Amano, who owned the hospital. He had been educated in the United States and been the physician for the American embassy before the war. It was clear that he was giving her special care.

"I'm feeling much better today, Doctor," Iva said. "I should be up and around in no time."

Now it was the doctor's turn to smile. "I don't think that's a good idea. Since this is not your first attack of these diseases, we need to get you strong before we release you. The food situation nationally is getting worse, and as a hospital, we have access to more rations and the fruits and vegetables you need. I think you should plan on being here for the next six weeks."

Filipe smiled. "Thank you. Finally someone who can tell this difficult American what she needs to do."

Iva frowned. "I don't know how I can afford that. I don't have much money, and I'm already borrowing from my landlady to pay my bills."

Amano leaned over his patient. "You cannot afford to leave here, since your health could be severely compromised. We'll work out a payment plan, and Filipe paid your expenses to date. The most important thing is you need to be as strong as possible before you are out there again, since you have no ration card."

Filipe stood up and looked at Iva. "I know you're going to be angry with me for paying without telling you, but I need you to get healthy. You can pay me back later when things are better."

Iva looked at the men. "I guess I don't have a choice.

Both of you, thanks for taking care of me." She reached over and squeezed Filipe's hand.

Amano said, "There's one more thing I want you to know. We'll get you well, but most people don't understand the long-term impact malnourishment has on our mental capabilities. Lack of enough food could affect your ability to think clearly and make good decisions for the rest of your life. You need to be aware of this when you're making decisions."

My thinking is fine. There's nothing wrong with it now, and there won't be in the future.

"Thanks, Dr. Amano. I'll keep that in mind."

⁂

THE SIX WEEKS IN DR. AMANO'S HOSPITAL FLEW BY. No trying to get home in the middle of the night on erratic streetcars and then rushing off to language school where she fought to stay awake. Filipe was there every day, sharing in hushed tones the latest war news monitored at Domei. With time to read and study, Iva's thoughts drifted to her family. She wondered how they were bearing up.

It was still hard for her to grasp that her America could lock up a whole race of people based upon bias and fear. Her family and the other Japanese Americans she grew up with wanted nothing more than a chance at a better life. Never in her life had Iva heard anything from her community other than a commitment to their adopted country. Now that her family was locked up, Iva felt sick whenever she thought about their situation.

Filipe's mother visited the hospital and started pushing Iva to visit more often and share Maria's food once she was released. Iva resisted, saying Maria could not afford to feed another mouth. The women went back and forth in this friendly argument. In the end, they agreed to see how circumstances developed and go from there.

As the end of Iva's hospitalization approached, she worried about how to maintain her health without a ration card. She concluded it would likely be a matter of time before her health deteriorated again. If this was the price she had to pay to stay loyal to the United States, so be it. In the meantime, she would enjoy the last few days of bed rest and get started on that new book Filipe brought.

IVA'S ENGLISH SKILLS WERE SO VALUED THAT HER JOB was still available when she left the hospital. On the third day back at work, she was having an especially bad time. After hearing the latest news Filipe brought about how bad conditions were in the US internment camps, gloom enveloped Iva. She prayed that conditions for her family were better there than here in militaristic Japan. At least back home, when the war was over, her family would be released and could return to a normal life. While Iva wanted to return to America, she was unsure how that would happen given her lack of money and whether the US State Department would ever recognize her citizenship.

When Iva returned to the boardinghouse that night, she found her room ransacked. Mrs. Furuya rushed up and apologized, saying she had not been able to stop the secret police from going through her things. It seemed this new group from Internal Security might be more serious compared to the relaxed visits of Fujiwara. Hopefully this would be the only time they came, since her landlady said the police had found nothing. Mrs. Furuya made sure to deliver her usual lecture about the men finding a better use for their time. Iva gave her landlady a big hug and thanked her for her protection.

Iva's anger and depression carried over to the next day at work. When she complained loudly about this harassment at her office, several coworkers took exception. "What did you expect when you refuse to become a citizen and help Japan?"

Soon Iva was in a toe-to-toe shouting match with a large colleague. When the angry man stepped forward, yelling at Iva and physically pushing her, mild-mannered Filipe rushed forward and punched the man in the face. The men were separated, and Gadow ordered everyone to calm down. "Everyone must forget this happened, or the secret police will visit us all." Gadow turned to Iva and Filipe, telling them to go home and come back when they could keep their tempers. "No more discussion about America and war here. Do you understand, Iva?"

Grabbing her things, Iva glared at her supervisor and headed for the door. Filipe took a minute to apologize to their boss. Once he caught up with Iva, who was stomping down the street, he grabbed her arm to slow her down. "That's just what the secret police need to hear about after searching your room yesterday. You start a fight about how the United States will win the war, and both of us will be in jail."

As they fell in step, she said, "I know I have to calm down, but this all gets to me. I want this war to end so I can go home."

Filipe reached out and stopped Iva in her tracks. "Sometimes I don't understand how a smart person like you cannot seem to learn. You're the most stubborn woman I've ever met. You know everyone at work except for us is for Japan, but you cannot keep your mouth shut. You trust that others won't retaliate. Well, Iva, there are lots of people out there who wouldn't mind hurting you when you act out. You've got to be more careful."

Iva looked at Filipe, recognizing he was right. *Why don't I stop and think rather than reacting when I'm upset? I know I'm my own worst enemy at times. Being stuck here is driving me crazy.* "I know you're saying this because you care, Fil. What do I do about this situation now?"

"You burned some bridges today. I don't know how you can go back to Domei again. Hopefully everyone will keep their mouths shut and the secret police will not get involved."

Iva smiled. "What about you going back there? You're the one who hit Yuki. By the way, did you see the look on his face after you smacked him? I've never seen anyone so surprised, especially since he's much bigger than you. My Sir Galahad rode to the rescue. Thank you."

Grinning, Filipe said, "I've wanted to do that for a long time, but I doubt that will affect my working there. You're the one who gets everyone riled up, and if I'm by myself, things will be okay. For you, it's time to get another job."

Iva nodded. "You're right. I'd better start looking."

CHAPTER 12

A few days later, Iva showed Filipe the ad she discovered in the *Nippon Times*. "Radio Tokyo wants typists who know English. I can do that."

"Since when do you know how to type?"

Iva smiled. "I have to type the reports at Domei. I admit I'm slow and only use two fingers, but if it's good enough where I am now, why would Radio Tokyo be any different? I certainly have the English part, and that must be harder for them to find than a good typist. What can it hurt to apply?"

"You Americans amaze me with your boldness. The job is for an experienced typist, and despite not knowing how to type with all your fingers, you think you have a chance."

"I can't afford to be as cautious and reserved as you. I'll never make ends meet unless I take some chances. Remember I had to borrow money from you and my landlady for the hospital bill. I need a job."

"I told you there's no need to pay me. Repay Mrs. Furuya first, and then we can discuss what you owe me if you insist."

"While I appreciate the loan, I'm responsible for my debts and will pay you back. I wonder if there's a place I might practice for the typing test mentioned in the article.

Wait, there's a typewriter at the language school. I bet they'll let me practice there."

⌒

ANOTHER SULTRY AUGUST DAY SETTLED OVER TOKYO, the kind Iva had come to dread. Already the humidity had soaked her blouse through. The streetcar taking her to Radio Tokyo was packed. Crammed in so close to people, Iva closed her eyes, trying to ignore the overwhelming smell of unwashed bodies. Ignoring the persistent headache she'd had for the past week, she thought back to Dr. Amano's warning about the long-term impacts of malnutrition. Now that adequate food was again an issue, Iva often struggled to stay focused and on task. *I hope this doesn't affect my new job.*

Today was her start at Radio Tokyo. Iva was proud to have somehow passed the typing test, especially since it was a way to show Filipe the value of taking chances. Pushing limits were second nature to Iva whether refusing to accept something her father prohibited or playing sports back home when other girls were studying home economics. Even though Filipe was now her closest friend, his passive approach to life bothered her.

The day before, she had dropped off another letter to her family with the Japanese Red Cross office. The nurse said they would try to get it to the United States like she always promised, but Red Cross correspondence was subject to government censorship, making final delivery unlikely. "As long as you try, that's all I can ask," Iva said. Sometimes she wondered why she kept wasting her time, but she refused to give up hope one of the letters might make it through.

This new streetcar route was taking her past the emperor's palace. As they got close, every passenger stood, faced the palace, and bowed deeply. Iva knew she shouldn't be surprised by the discipline and commitment ingrained in Japan's citizens, but it bothered her nonetheless. She was soon the only passenger sitting down. Once past the palace, several passengers turned and yelled at her for not showing respect. The verbal abuse spread. An older woman standing next to Iva roughly bumped into her and shook her fist in the American's face. When the streetcar reached the next stop, Iva pushed her way out. The angry calls faded as the car started up again.

Trembling, Iva was frightened by how quickly the passengers turned on her. She had promised Filipe to be on her best behavior at the new job and to avoid discussing the war. Relieved he was not here to see this scene, Iva set off at a brisk pace to arrive at Radio Tokyo on time. She needed a new streetcar route, since she'd be damned if she was ever going to bow when passing the emperor's palace.

WHILE HER NEW JOB WAS IN A BUILDING THAT LOOKED nice from the outside, Iva looked at a worn and poorly maintained office space. In her typing area, the furniture was old and rickety with desks pushed almost on top of each other. Even a small woman like Iva could reach out on either side and touch her coworkers. Dark-brown walls added to the oppressive atmosphere of an office long gone to ruin. The stifling air in the closed building made her uncomfortable, but like everyone around her, she kept her head down, determined to make a good first impression.

When Yuchi Hirakawa showed her to her desk, her boss got straight to the point. "It is obvious you do not know how to type well, but we need people who have your English skills. Concentrate on improving your typing." Then he was gone.

She scanned the rough broadcast script a Japanese writer had translated into basic English. It was Iva's job to make it readable in terminology Americans commonly used. Iva was stunned at how poorly written it was. The language was stilted and formal and didn't reflect how Americans expected announcers to sound on the radio. Then there was the content itself. She was working in the radio station's American section where the mission was to broadcast Japanese propaganda to American troops stationed in the Pacific. As part of this script, the announcer was to read Shinto prayers. *Is this script supposed to get American soldiers and sailors to listen? If this is the best the Japanese can do, there's no possibility any of this propaganda will have an impact, and there's no way I'm going to make it more effective. I'll change a few words and concentrate on learning to type.*

A bit later, Iva looked up and saw two women standing in front of her. "We wondered if you'd ever discover us. When someone types as slowly as you, I can understand why you have to concentrate," one of them said. The women giggled. The speaker extended her arm and said in English, "Hi. I'm Ruth Hayakawa, and this is June Suyama. We're both announcers, and we wanted to meet the new typist who will improve the translations so our broadcasts can be better. We're going to get some tea. Would you like to join us?"

Standing, Iva stretched her cramped muscles. "I'm not sure I should take a break, since this is my first day."

"Don't worry about Yuchi. If he sees you're meeting with announcers, he won't complain. He might when he sees how slowly you type. Never mind, come on. We heard you're an American, and we want to hear how you ended up here."

Once settled at the broken-down tables in the break room, Iva learned Ruth was born in Japan, and her family moved to America when she was still a baby. Ruth stayed in the United States while attending junior college in the Los Angeles area. Unable to find a good job because of the Depression, she moved back to Japan and took this job. Ruth was an extremely attractive woman who was taller than most. With her lilting speech, Iva thought she was just the type of announcer the Japanese thought Americans would listen to: a soft, female voice with an American accent to remind them of home.

June was also pretty but not nearly as tall as Ruth. She was also native-born Japanese but moved with her parents to British Columbia, where she grew up. Returning to Japan before the war, June was one of the longest-employed female announcers. Her low, sultry voice brought her the on-air name of "The Nightingale of Nanjing."

It was Iva's turn to tell her story. "Poor timing got me stuck here. I'm sure my father regrets how this worked out. What worries me most is that I don't know what my family is going through in one of those internment camps." Iva's eyes filled with tears.

Ruth reached over and held Iva's hand, but June seemed put off by Iva's story. June said belligerently, "Have you become a Japanese citizen? If not, why?"

"No war talk in this office," Ruth said. "Whatever any of us want or choose to do, so be it."

June gave Ruth an angry look but said no more.

Ruth turned to Iva. "We need to get back to work, especially so you can get us some decent copy to read on air."

Smiling, Iva said nothing about the miserable material she was working with and her decision to do little about it. "I'll do my best, and thanks for coming by to introduce yourselves. Are there other female announcers I should meet?"

Ruth said, "There are almost twenty women who do broadcasts. We'll be sure to introduce you to everyone. It's nice to meet you, and let us know if there's anything we might do to help."

"One last question," Iva said. "Is there a place in the break room where I could store my lunch?"

Ruth and June looked at each other, taking in the innocence of the question. Ruth gently answered, "If you bring food for lunch, keep it close at all times. People here are getting hungrier and more desperate every day."

When she returned to her desk, Iva saw her boss watching from across the room. With her head down, she concentrated on trying to make up for the time off. In a moment, she noticed Ruth was back. Leaning close, Ruth whispered, "Be careful what you say about the war around here and where your sympathies lie. There are numerous secret police. Be especially careful with June. She is one hundred percent pro-Japanese and has the bite of a viper."

THE NEXT DAY, IVA NOTICED TWO WESTERNERS AND A Filipino touring the station. All three wore raggedy clothes that, in some places, didn't cover their bodies. Open sores were visible on their arms and hands. The Westerners looked especially emaciated and ill.

Iva guessed that they might be Americans, and a wave of excitement ran through her. It was rare to see other Westerners since the war started, and they were probably prisoners of war. Her interest was high, since these were the first possible countrymen she had seen in years. Then they were gone. Iva made up her mind to learn more about them and figure out how to make contact.

As soon as she could justify a break, Iva looked for Ruth to see if she had any information about the prisoners. Ruth pulled the American close. "Look, you have to be careful around here. Stay away from them, or you could get in trouble. Yes, they're prisoners and are all experienced in radio. They've been brought here to improve our weak broadcasts and create something Americans might listen to. One is Australian. He's the tall one. The other white is an American, and the third is from the Philippines. They're here to put together a new program called the *Zero Hour*."

"Where do they work? I want to talk to them."

"Are you listening to me? Don't be stupid. They have an office on the floor below us, but you should stay away."

"Thanks. I will." Iva rushed back to her desk. *One American. I wonder where he lives back home.*

DURING HER AFTERNOON BREAK, IVA HUSTLED DOWN to the second floor and found the small office where the prisoners were working. With no Japanese around, Iva drew a deep breath to screw up her courage and headed into the office. As the three men turned their heads, Iva extended her hand and said, "Hi, I'm Iva Toguri from the United States. I got stuck here once the war started. Keep your chins up." She shook their hands and spun on her heels to leave. Glancing back as she fled, she saw that they looked puzzled.

Back at her desk, Iva carefully looked around to see if anyone was going to question what she'd done. It appeared no one had seen her visit, so she calmed down. She remembered the looks on their faces as she was leaving. *Might they think I was a spy for the Japanese? Oh well, I'll figure out how to visit them again and show I'm on their side.*

A COUPLE WEEKS LATER WHEN IVA AGAIN VISITED THE second-floor POWs, she found Major Charles Cousens alone. By now, she had met with the prisoners several times, so her visits were becoming a regular occurrence. Japanese staff in the office started to ask her what project she'd been assigned to work on with the prisoners. Iva answered with a general statement that her work concerned the *Zero Hour* radio program, and beyond that, she was not free to discuss details.

When she explained this cover story to Cousens, he smiled. "Good on you. To be honest, when you first sashayed in here and said I'm from America, we thought for sure you were a spy. We decided to stay away from you at first. Now we're convinced you're not a spy, and instead, you're a lady with some real backbone."

Iva learned Cousens was a major in the Australian army and had been a famous radio announcer in Sydney before he enlisted to fight the Japanese. With the rank of major, he was the senior prisoner at the Bunka POW Camp in Tokyo and responsible for all prisoners there. At forty, Cousens embodied the classic English gentleman with his perfect posture, small mustache, and impeccable manners. Born in England, he joined the army once he completed school and served in India. After being discharged, Cousens emigrated, looking for new opportunities. He was now a citizen of Australia and married with two children.

The American POW was Captain Ted Ince, a redhead with deep-blue eyes and a bushy mustache. He towered over Iva. Born in Spokane, Washington, he had worked in radio after graduating from Washington State University. Ince brought his experience in radio to the army at the start of the war and was doing broadcasts for the military in Manila until he was captured. Before imprisonment, he met and married a Filipino who was still in that country along with their son.

Lieutenant Norman Reyes of the Philippine army was the third POW and served on Ince's staff. Born of an American mother and Filipino father and boyishly handsome at nineteen, he was the youngest of the three. Reyes had limited radio experience but was passionate about the medium. He spoke openly about doing anything to avoid more of the harsh treatment the Japanese put him through after capture. Not long after the prisoners arrived at Radio Tokyo, Japan announced the occupied Philippines would be a republic under Japanese supervision. Since there was no longer an official state of war with the Philippines, Reyes was released as a POW and became a paid employee of Radio Tokyo. He remained assigned to work on the team with Cousens and Ince.

Describing her experiences in Japan to Cousens, Iva said, "It's been tough at times to stand up to the Japanese. While they haven't thrown me in jail, if they did, I wouldn't have to scrounge for food all the time. It seems like no matter what Fil and I do, there is never enough to eat. The constant hunger is the worst part of being here."

Cousens nodded. "I agree. It's the same way for all the prisoners. The Japanese keep making cuts, so we receive less food and medicine almost every week."

"I suspected as prisoners you get less food than civilians in Japan. Since the government keeps cutting rations for their citizens, I imagine it must be terrible for everyone at Bunka. I notice you've lost another tooth and your gums are bleeding again. Is that from lack of food?"

"Most likely. It's bad for us, but you can't be doing much better, since you don't even have a ration card. You're all skin and bones."

"At least Fil and I can get out into the country on weekends and trade on the black market. Next time we go out there, I'll see what I might bring you. Is there anything you particularly need?"

"That's generous, but you need to take care of yourself first. However, if you're able to get some medicines, there are about thirty prisoners at Bunka who are sick and suffering greatly. We have a couple close to death, and one recently died. It tears me up the men suffer so and I can do so little to help them. Anything you can find, even as simple as aspirin, would be appreciated."

"I'm sure I can find aspirin, and I'll see what other medicines might be available. Two weeks ago, someone was selling quinine for malaria. Will you be able to smuggle anything I bring back into your camp?"

"We'll have to figure out a way to sneak things in, but leave that to us."

"How is the preparation for *Zero Hour* going? I see the Japanese appointed a program manager for you, George Mitsushio. I thought you were going to be in charge."

"I thought it was my show, but Major Tsuneishi, the army commander here, doesn't trust us POWs. George and his assistant, Kenkichi Oki, are here to keep an eye on us. Since both attended school in the United States, it'll be challenging to hoodwink them, but I'm confident we can figure out ways to sabotage the broadcasts. Both of them had to come back to Japan since they couldn't find jobs in the States after college, so they can't be all that sharp."

Iva remembered Ruth providing background on the *Zero Hour* program managers. Both kept their American citizenship while also registering in Japan, and Ruth said if Japan lost the war, Mitsushio and Oki would be in serious trouble with the United States.

Watching the Australian complete some paperwork, Iva realized Cousins' can-do attitude and priority for the well-being of the men reporting to him made him someone she could emulate. When the Australian looked up, Iva said, "If you're going to smuggle medicine into Bunka, we might as well also get some food for the men."

It was Cousens' turn to smile. "If you can get some food, there are many men who could benefit. By the way, I assume your boss bought your story that you've been drafted to work on the *Zero Hour*. No pushback there?"

"One thing about the Japanese is they hate to question authority, whether real or perceived. I know you'll back me up if someone asks, but that reminds me that I'd better get back upstairs. I'll see you tomorrow."

Back at her desk, Iva thought about the need for medicine and food for the POWs and what Mrs. Furuya said about thinking of others. *Helping Charles and the prisoners is where I can make a difference in this war. Now that my finances are more settled, I have some extra money. I'm going to do all I can to get what the POWs need even if I have to do without. Fil won't like it, since there will be some risk, but this is my duty as an American.*

Iva found Cousens' story of how he ended up at Radio Tokyo fascinating. After capture, he tried to hide his radio background, but the Japanese discovered who he was from another prisoner. When the Japanese told him he was being sent to Tokyo to do broadcasts, he refused, resulting in severe beatings. He was brought to Radio Tokyo under the threat of execution if he did not cooperate. Major Tsuneishi even took out his sword and moved it menacingly in front of his prisoner. Cousens decided it was time to give in. Now he planned to sabotage the broadcasts he was forced to put together.

"How are you going to do that?" Iva said.

"I'm not sure, and I imagine it'll be a day-to-day thing depending on the circumstances. As you know, most Japanese working here don't understand how American and English soldiers and sailors think and talk. Slipping in a few keywords or how an announcer says something would tell a listener this isn't serious. Here's one idea I've been thinking of. What if we're announcing a Japanese victory, and every time that battle is mentioned the announcer chuckles? I bet the Japanese wouldn't pick up that hidden message."

Iva nodded and brought up something that had been on her mind. "I've got a question about Captain Ince. You've told me he's one hundred percent committed to sabotaging the broadcasts, as am I, but whenever I'm around, all I sense is hostility from him."

Looking Iva directly in the eye, Cousens said, "You've got to give Teddy a break. The Japanese did terrible things to him and his men in the Philippines. Although he knows you're American and we can trust you, when he looks at you, all he sees is a Japanese face. Keep your distance, and don't take it personally."

"Okay. I'll try, and thanks for explaining." Still, Ince's attitude worried her. She hoped it would not lead to problems down the road.

Cousens said, "Let's get back to something positive. The Domei news you and Filipe share that I bring to the POWs is making a big difference with morale at Bunka. For my suffering men to know the war has turned and the Japanese are on the defensive is almost as important as food. Please thank Filipe for me."

"I'll do that." *Maybe I won't pass along that message. Fil is increasingly critical of danger in helping the POWs, but the risks are worth it and something I must do no matter what Fil thinks.*

CHAPTER 13

Iva was typing the final *Zero Hour* script on March 20, 1943, the day the program was set to begin. Her editing of the script confirmed that Cousens' strategies were in play. The program was primarily entertainment. That focus took some time to get past Major Tsuneishi, but eventually he agreed. There was also a significant portion of the program with updates on POWs and their status, so families back home could receive news about their loved ones. At the end of the broadcast, there were a few minutes of news. Cousens himself would do that announcing and incorporate wording that alerted listeners as to what was actually going on.

Looking up from her typewriter, Iva was surprised to see the Australian major striding to her desk accompanied by a guard. "Mornin', Iva. We've got a problem. The announcer who was going to do the music section of *Zero Hour* had a falling out with the army and was removed from the program. We need someone right away to introduce the music, and I think you'd be terrific doing that. Are you willing to help?"

Iva felt a knot form in her stomach. She knew nothing about radio and only wanted this typing job that let her stay invisible. Filipe would be upset if she agreed to do broadcasts. Might there be a risk back in the States? If she became an announcer, might the Allies consider that treason?

"No way. I don't want to do broadcasts. There are lots of other female announcers who can do this. Go get Ruth."

"I'm not going to take no for an answer. I need your help, and you'd be perfect. You stay here while I talk to your supervisor about letting you join us downstairs to get ready for tonight's broadcast." With that, Cousens headed over to her supervisor's office.

The knot in Iva's stomach grew, but she didn't know what to do. Maybe her boss would object, since he would lose a typist. She prayed that he would show some backbone.

BEFORE IVA KNEW IT, SHE WAS SITTING IN FRONT OF A microphone. Removing her headphones and looking around the broadcast studio, she was impressed by all of the electronic gear. Several pieces of new equipment told her this was the part of the radio station where investments took place. During rehearsals, she noticed how quiet the studio was compared to her typing pool.

Cousens was outside the open door, preparing to come in and give her more coaching. She heard Ince talking quietly with the major, which Iva had no trouble hearing.

"I don't get you, Major. She's inexperienced and has that god-awful squeaky voice. There are lots of professional women here with voices suited to radio. What're you trying to prove?"

"That's why she's perfect, Ted. If we're trying to sabotage the broadcasts, her voice is a good one for listeners to know this can't be a serious broadcast."

Ince shook his head. "I hope you know what you're doing. If Tsuneishi gets wind of your intent, there'll be hell to pay, and I don't want to be near that fallout."

"Don't worry. I'll take full responsibility if it blows up. I'll make sure none of this lands on you or Reyes."

With a dismissive shrug, Ince turned and walked away. Returning to Iva, Cousens said, "Let's take it from the top again. All you're doing is introducing these records and saying a few words about each. There's nothing political or about the war, so you don't have to worry about consequences from the Japanese. I know you're worried, but I'll make sure you never do anything to compromise your US citizenship. I'm always here to protect you."

Hearing these words, Iva calmed down. A few moments ago her boss had informed her she was transferred full time to the radio staff, so what choice did she have? *If my voice is part of the plan to sabotage the broadcasts, so be it. Do I have a squeaky voice? Is my voice that awful? No one ever told me my voice was terrible.*

"One more time from the top, Iva. After the introduction of *Zero Hour*, you'll be next. Read the script, and remember, don't rush. The audience needs to hear each word, since long-distance broadcasts often have a lot of static. Ready? Let's begin."

⌒‾‾‾

COUSENS' FINGERS COUNTED DOWN TO WHEN SHE should start. Iva's stomach was full of butterflies, but she was determined to follow the major's instructions to the letter. As she glanced down at the script, none of the words struck her as risky. Wetting her lips one last time, she saw three, two, one, and then his index finger pointing at her.

"Hello to all boneheads in the Pacific. Welcome to Radio Tokyo's special program of music during the *Zero Hour*. We're going to start tonight with the Boston Pops to be followed by melodies of Stephen Foster. The performers of Foster's music were typically wandering minstrels, the orphans of the South. Just like you American soldiers and sailors, we're now orphans of the Pacific, but first, let's enjoy as the Boston Pops get us started with 'Strike Up the Band.'"

As the record started playing, Iva looked up to see Cousens giving her a big smile and thumbs-up. Iva took a deep breath of relief. *That wasn't so bad. I hope my voice was squeaky enough.*

AFTER HER PART OF THE PROGRAM WAS DONE, EVERYONE congratulated Iva, including George Mitsushio and Kenkichi Oki. Neither of the program managers complained about the quality of her announcing or using the word "bonehead" in her script. They applauded her for being a permanent part of the program.

Cousens appeared after reading the news announcements. Iva had seen the script for the news. There was nothing that could be deemed critical by the Allies. Maybe the Australian was going to pull off his sabotage. As everyone else was leaving, Iva asked, "Charles, how did the Japanese come up with the name Zero Hour? Does it mean anything?"

"The Japanese think it'll strike terror into the hearts of the Americans. First, Zeros are the Japanese's best fighting aircraft. Second, they believe there's a strong implication for Zero Hour being when the Japanese win the war and the Americans will be defeated. Like that's ever going to happen."

Iva smiled. "If you don't need me anymore, I'll head home and tell Fil about my new job. What time do you want me here tomorrow?"

"Around ten. We have all day to get ready for the evening broadcast. By the way, since you're going to be a regular, you should pick an on-air name that listeners will get to know. Sleep on it, and see what you can come up with."

"I think I already have one. When I was speaking today about the orphans of the Pacific, it hit home that I'm one. Back home, Orphan Annie is a popular comic strip. What if I call myself Orphan Ann of the Pacific?"

"I like it."

When she got back to her desk in the main room, she could see that the papers were scattered and ink was spilled on everything. She felt a moment of anger and then shrugged it off. *It looks like someone was not happy with my broadcast.*

IVA LOWERED HER HEAD AS FILIPE WENT OVER HIS ARGU-ments again. For such a mild-mannered guy, at times he would not back off. Wishing he would let it go, she repeated that Cousens could be trusted and had promised to protect her. She was going to do this job no matter what Filipe thought.

"You should have said no, Iva. It sounds like you did initially, but then you gave in. Maybe you could back out tomorrow and go back to your old job."

"Fil, I've had enough. I don't get to do what I want at Radio Tokyo, and my boss told me I was permanently transferred to the broadcast staff. You worry too much. I know how to take care of myself, and I'm tired of arguing."

After he was quiet for a moment, Filipe continued. "Remember what Dr. Amano said about decision making being affected by poor eating? Maybe you should take a day or two to decide about becoming an announcer."

Iva felt a surge of anger and almost leaped out of her chair. "My decision making is fine. Don't say there is something wrong with me, and don't mention how stubborn I am like you always do. I'm not a child, and I know what's best for me. I'm not some traditional Japanese woman you think you can push around."

Fil bit his lip. "All right, I'll let it go, but remember, some people might think you're helping the Japanese too much and could be charged with treason after the war. That's what I worry about."

"As I said, you worry too much. I'll be fine."

CHAPTER 14

"Okay, Lars, I'm late and have to get running. See you tomorrow."

"All right, Iva. Have a good evening, but someday I'm going to make you tell me why you seem to turn into a pumpkin at four-thirty each afternoon."

"Sure," she said over her shoulder as she hurried out of the Danish Ministry. Iva was late and would have to rush to get to Radio Tokyo in time for rehearsal with Cousens. It would be nice to have more time between her jobs, but given how lucrative it was to be the secretary to the Danish Minister, it would have to be.

She had seen the ad in a newspaper two months before. As with the Radio Tokyo possibility, Filipe scoffed that Iva wasn't qualified, yet she got the job. Only yesterday the tall, blond minister with glasses, Lars Tillitse, told her how well she was doing despite not knowing shorthand. Iva laughed to herself, remembering the interview when the minister asked about her shorthand skills. She said she could do that. The look he gave indicated he knew Iva was lying, but he gave her the job anyway.

Besides the extra money that allowed her to improve her finances, the real bonus was that the Ministry received diplomatic-level rations. The pantry was always well stocked, and Tillitse generously allowed Iva to take food and medicines without too many questions. He thought the food was for Iva, Filipe, and his mother, but in reality, most of the supplies were going to Cousens' fellow POWs.

Filipe was still worried about Iva's health. "With all the food you take from the Ministry, you're still not eating enough. Have you considered that if you get sick you'll be of no help to the POWs? I wonder if the lack of food is affecting your decision making."

"I'm doing okay, and our household has enough to eat. The POWs need it more, and they are my number one priority, so quit harping on me."

Iva was now living in Maria's house, and in that small, traditional Japanese residence, there was no getting away from Filipe's lectures. It had taken a lot of pressure for Iva to agree to the move, but the financial pressure caused by spending so much money on the black market decided the issue. Since three people slept in the communal room, there was limited opportunity for sex, although Filipe pushed his futon close every night. While initially reluctant to be intimate, Iva was comfortable at this stage of their relationship.

The downside of living in Maria's house was that Iva's commute took two and a half hours each way. That meant she was up at 5:00 and on to the Danish Ministry. At 4:30 in the afternoon, she rushed to Radio Tokyo. Shortly after 7:00, following her part of the broadcast, she stood in lines to try to get hard-to-find items from the few merchants still operating in the city. Most nights she arrived home well after 10:00. Then there were the weekend trips to the country. It was a schedule she was determined to stick with no matter how exhausting.

Other than burning the candle on both ends, Iva was enjoying this living arrangement. Filipe and his mother appreciated the extra food, while Iva and Maria grew closer day by day. Iva also got to know Jose, Filipe's father. He dropped in from time to time to spend a few days, and he liked Iva. There were gently dropped hints about wedding bells from the parents. *That's not something I'm going to deal with right now,* she thought.

This morning as she rushed to the Ministry from the streetcar, Iva noticed the bomb damage was getting worse. Only a month before, the Allies captured an island so close that bombers could reach Tokyo. There were not many days now when Tokyo and other major Japanese cities would escape air raids. The Allies seemed to have plans for sectors of the city where they wanted to concentrate attacks, so this part of town was almost total rubble. Areas such as where Radio Tokyo was located remained untouched for which Iva was grateful. Passing another pile of debris, Iva gagged at the sight of an arm extending from a collapsed building. Dead bodies were increasingly common as was the growing delay in the collection of the deceased. Closing her eyes and hurrying on, Iva knew she could never get used to this horror.

Stopping a block later to regain her equilibrium, Iva thought how common it was now for her to wake in a cold sweat thinking she was under rubble and screaming for her mother and father. On those nights, she woke to find Maria stroking her head to calm her.

Despite the horrible effects, Iva also thought the Allied bombing was a fascinating sight. The previous weekend when she and Filipe went to visit friends on the other side of the river, they all went outside to watch the bombers attacking Tokyo. The explosions reminded her of the Fourth of July at home when her birthday party ended with fireworks. Here, searchlights lit up the skies, creating waving beams while the anti-aircraft fire added explosive bursts. The planes dropped their bombs, lighting up the skyline as they exploded. Fires followed, and it all made the ground rumble. Occasionally a plane was hit and exploded. Even though it was terrible, Iva found she couldn't turn away.

A dozen blocks later and now in an unbombed neighborhood, Iva arrived at the Danish Ministry. Entering the old building and closing the door, she felt the contrast of the suffering outside and the stately quiet within. It was like stepping back into the world where she grew up. There were elegant high ceilings, rich wood, and a broad staircase to the upstairs meeting rooms. *I feel safe here. Why can't all of my life be like this? I'm so tired of the stress from this war and how it impacts everything.*

Iva found Tillitse in the kitchen pouring coffee, and he started a cup for his secretary. "Good morning, Lars. I have a surprise for you. Last night I got lucky. See what I found?" Iva pulled three cigars from her bag.

"My goodness, where did you get these? You must have incredible connections to find them. Thank you so much."

"Now you see where some of the food and medicine is going."

"Don't worry about what you take. We've more than I need here. Where are my matches so I can get one of these lit up?"

Between the minister and Filipe's mother, Iva felt like

she had surrogate parents looking out for her. On top of that, she was starting to like being a radio announcer. The program was getting popular, and the length of the broadcast kept expanding. Now she was on air twenty minutes per show and playing up to five records sandwiched between her short remarks. She asked Cousens if she might have a future in broadcasting back in the United States. The Australian gently said it would be best if Iva focused on another field. *Guess I still have a squeaky voice. No matter. These are the best circumstances for me since I arrived in Japan. If I ignore the bombing, it's almost tolerable.*

That afternoon, Iva rushed into the broadcast area where Cousens was waiting for her. She was surprised to see him in a new business suit rather than his tattered uniform. "Look at you, new clothes and all. What's the special occasion, and why couldn't you get something that fits? That suit is way too big especially since you've lost so much weight."

Cousens laughed. "Management thought I needed to look more professional, so they sent me to the clothing store. I had to argue with the salesman to get this suit. By having it so large, there's lots of room to smuggle in the food and medicine you're getting us."

"Pretty smart, but you look like some character from a bad movie."

"That's the first time anyone said I resemble a movie star, so I'll take that as a compliment. Now here's your script. Take a look, and let's go over it. By the way, does your Danish minister still not know you're working here?"

Iva shook her head. "No. I think it's better to leave well enough alone. He might not like me doing broadcasts, and

I can't afford to lose that job now that I'm helping the guys at Bunka."

"What you're doing is making a real difference. More than one of our boys is alive because of you."

A warm glow filled her heart. "Glad to hear that. By the way, Fil mentioned last night that Italy surrendered to the Allies a couple of days ago. The Germans are rushing in troops to occupy Italy, but at least there's one country that's dropped out of the war."

"That's terrific news, and it will lift spirits with the POWs tonight. It's still a long way to go to defeat Germany, but that's great progress. Did you get a chance to hear the new American radio program to the Japanese people now that the Allies are close enough to broadcast?"

"I did yesterday. It was lame and reminded me of how poor the Japanese broadcasts were before you took over. Since you've been successful in minimizing the propaganda, it's apparent that people in the Pacific are listening. If the Americans broadcasting from Saipan understood your approach, maybe more people would listen here, and those Allied broadcasts would be more effective."

"Air time is approaching, so let's get started rehearsing."

As Iva looked over her lines for the evening, she wondered if Cousens would ever let her write her own scripts. Every time she brought the subject up, the major said he could protect her only by making sure someone else was doing the writing. That way she could argue that she was forced to read what others wrote.

They looked closely at tonight's script. Sitting so close, Iva felt a strong attraction for this man. *He's the reason I'm able to make a positive contribution to the war effort, and he's promised to protect me. This man pushes back against the Japanese even in the worst of circumstances. His strength is something I admire, but I can't think of him as anyone but a colleague. I'm sexually involved with Fil and don't need to complicate my life more than it already is. Besides, Charles is happily married. Still, this guy is something. I wonder how I'd feel if I'd met Charles before Fil came into my life.*

"Hey, daydreamer, concentrate. Here's the spot in the broadcast where we're going to try something different."

"Sorry. Let's go over that again."

CHAPTER 15
1943-1944

The cold was setting in with Christmas fast approaching. Iva hated this time of year the most. With so little central heating in Japanese homes and the war shortages, even buildings like the one Radio Tokyo occupied had intermittent heat. The bleak and growing bombed-out landscape of Tokyo contributed to a growing sense of hopelessness.

What was especially troubling was that Cousens suffered two heart attacks and was hospitalized. Iva managed to get into his ward to visit only after much pushing, and she was shocked to see his condition. She knew he was thin under that oversized suit. To see his skeletal frame lying helpless and him struggling to speak made her feel like the world was falling apart. Here was the man who was supposed to protect her, and he could barely lift his head off the pillow. What was going to happen at Radio Tokyo now?

Iva smiled. "I snuck some fruit and bread in. Let me slip it under your pillow for when no one is around. I'm not sure I'll be able to visit again, but if I can, is there anything you want me to bring you?"

Cousens spoke in a voice Iva had to lean closer to hear. "Don't worry about me. What you brought will taste good.

I'm already eating a little better. The doctor admits my heart attacks were due to a lack of food and stress. What's most important is for you to try to get anything you can scrounge into Bunka."

"I'll give it a go, but with Ted gone, I no longer see someone every day from the camp."

"It's unfortunate Ted got shipped out. See if you can find another contact. Even if you can't, what you've done has already saved many lives, but you have to be careful. There are more spies around than ever."

"I know, and someone at the station has it in for me. I continue to get harassing notes saying I'm being watched and threatening me. It scares me to be there without you. Mitsushio and Oki are flexing their muscles as the program managers. Major Tsuneishi is saying that *Zero Hour* doesn't have enough propaganda, and that's one of the reasons the war is going badly. Reyes is still there, but he seems willing to do whatever the Japanese want. I feel utterly alone."

Cousens raised his hand and put it on her arm. Iva felt that there was no strength in it. "You must protect yourself. If they start filling the broadcasts with propaganda, you need to avoid being part of that. Tell them you'll only introduce records. If they slip something into your script, misread it or reword it. Should you get in trouble, maybe the best thing would be to get fired."

"I've thought the same thing, although I doubt they'd let me resign. Perhaps I should stop showing up for work. I could use the bombing and long commute as an excuse. The Japanese still don't know about my job at the Danish Ministry, so I'd have that income. I could even say Filipe wants me home more, since we're planning to get married."

"Are you engaged? If so, congratulations. I'm happy for the two of you."

"No, we're not formally engaged even though that topic comes up more and more. I could use engagement as part of my cover story, but then maybe I should go ahead with the real thing."

Cousens paused. "Do you love him? Are you sure you want to get married to deal with your employment problem?"

Iva closed her eyes and thought about the question she'd never expected from the Australian. She said, "I think I love him. He's been the one to stand by me along with you. His family has been good to me and supportive of my being a loyal American. Yeah, I think I love him."

"Well then, I'm happy for you no matter what you decide. Filipe is a decent fellow, although from what you've told me, he doesn't like you being a risk taker. Being married means you might have to compromise more than you like."

"Taking chances is not Fil's nature, but he puts up with me. Compromise and listening more to Filipe—that's something I have to work on." Iva smiled, patted his hand, and placed it on the sheet. "I have to head out soon, as the streetcars are getting more erratic because of the bombing. You need to take care of yourself and make sure you're resting so you can come back to keep your eye on me. I need you, Major, and so do the prisoners who report to you." She bent down and gave him a big hug and kiss on the cheek.

As Iva started to pull away, Cousens reached out and pulled her back. "Remember what we discussed about the war. These are awful times, but they will pass. Don't let the hate and despair all around us take you over. There are lessons from these bad days we can learn that will make the rest of our lives better. You're a good person. Be kind to yourself."

As he let her go, Iva gave him one final kiss and headed for the door. "I'll check back when I can, Major. In the meantime, take care."

Outside the hospital room, she leaned against the wall as her eyes filled with tears. She choked back a sob and fought to control her feelings. *Will Charles recover? What was he trying to say to me about learning from my situation? I want this war to be over so I can go back to my life the way it used to be. Might this be the last time I see him? Without Charles to look over me and the changes taking place at Radio Tokyo, I'm scared.*

⌒

"Don't sit there and say nothing. You've not been to work here for over a week, and suddenly we're graced by your presence. Do you know how hard it is to have to fill in for you at the last minute? Others at the station have been complaining about where the American is. Why does she get to stay home while we have to work? We're lucky Miyeko has been able to cover for you, but we need to rely on you. Do you understand?"

Mitsushio was worked up. In the corner, Oki sat quietly watching Iva squirm. His wry smile made her furious.

Damn these two. Why did I even bother to show up today? "George, I told you that with the bombing and all the damage to the streetcars, it's been impossible to get here. Filipe wants me to be safe and spend more time with his mother. Maybe it'd be best if I quit and you get someone reliable."

"You cannot quit. There's a war going on, and we need you more than ever. Major Tsuneishi is adamant you stay. He knows you're here, and he wants to speak with you. After our talk, we'll take you to his office."

Iva's heart sank. Being brought to the senior military officer of Radio Tokyo couldn't be good. Maybe she'd pushed this too far. She remembered Cousens' story about being threatened by Tsuneishi's battle sword. What if they arrested her and threw her in jail? What was the best way to respond now?

"I see that the idea of visiting the major quieted your tongue. Good. As far as the bombing goes, we all must deal with that. You're not married, so what do I care what your boyfriend wants? You need to be here, do you understand?"

"Yes, I understand."

"Okay, let's go see the major where you can tell him of your commitment to *Zero Hour*."

A few minutes later, they were standing outside Tsuneishi's office. After he called them in, the major spoke to Iva's managers. "You two can go back to work. I want to speak with Iva alone."

The men gave Iva an angry look as they left.

"Please, Iva, sit down. Would you like some tea?"

"No, thank you, Major. I'm fine."

"I think some tea is what we both need. Our offices are colder now since we must make more sacrifices for the army." Stepping to the door, the major barked an order to his secretary, who was soon back with a pot of tea and two cups. After pouring tea for the American, the major sat back and took a long sip of his tea. "Ah, soothing. Don't you agree?"

Iva put her cup down. "Yes, Major. It's good. Thank you for being so thoughtful."

"We have missed you, Iva. Have you been well?"

Wetting her lips, she said, "Not really. The bombing makes it difficult to get here, especially now that I live with the mother of a friend because of expenses. Under the best of circumstances, it's almost three hours each way, and every day it seems like there's more damage to the streetcar system. I don't like being out when the bombing is going on, since attacks are now close to this building."

"We are all suffering, and for how much longer I don't know." The major again took a long sip of tea.

For how much longer? Was the major implying the war was not going well and Japan would lose? Should I respond to this statement?

Tsuneishi started again. "We need you here, Iva. You are one of our most important announcers. It is apparent *Zero Hour* is our most listened-to radio program, and Orphan Ann of the Pacific is an important part of the program's success."

"Thank you, Major. As I told George and Kenkichi, maybe it's better if I quit so you can get a reliable announcer. They said Miyeko has been doing a good job. Maybe she should be permanent."

"No, Iva, we need you. You cannot quit. Do you understand? My superiors are telling me we must do more with the *Zero Hour*. This program is critical to the war effort, and you are a major reason for its success. I don't want to hear you speak of quitting ever again. Am I clear?"

Swallowing hard, Iva said, "Yes, Major."

"Good. Now you say you have to live so far away because of money, so today I am doubling your salary. You are now the highest-paid female announcer. Maybe this will allow you to move closer and make it easier to get to work. We all must put up with the bombing your countrymen are inflicting upon innocent Japanese."

Iva tried to process what she was hearing. *I'm directly ordered to do this job, although so far, there is no direct threat of jail or torture like Cousens experienced. If I continue to refuse, the major is likely to go there, since it's apparent he's not going to accept no. This man scares me like nothing I've ever experienced, and I want to get out of here as quickly as possible. Best to figure out what to do away from Tsuneishi.*

"Thank you, Major. That's very generous of you. I'm thankful."

"Good. Now finish your tea. You need to rehearse for today's broadcast. I will watch you today since we have missed you so much."

Iva gulped down the tea and left the major's office. Once back in the broadcast area, Mitsushio and Kenkichi were waiting, wearing Cheshire cat grins. Mitsushio said, "How did things go with the major? I'm sure you can see how you need to be more responsible around here."

"Major Tsuneishi doubled my salary."

"What?" Mitsushio sputtered. "That will not sit well with the other announcers."

"That's your problem, George. Now I must go over my script. The major said he'd come to watch my broadcast, so I must prepare."

IT WAS CLOSE TO BROADCAST TIME, AND IVA WAS STRUG-
gling with some of the wording the program managers
put in her script. She wasn't sure there was a problem,
but it was apparent these words were an effort at more
propaganda. Because of Filipe's work at Domei, Iva knew
that over a month ago, the Battle of Leyte Gulf had been a
smashing Allied victory. While both sides lost ships, the
Japanese navy's fighting capability was destroyed, yet here
in the script was language that spoke of a Japanese victory,
claiming that all the American ships were sunk and many
Allied soldiers and sailors were stranded. She tried several
times with her managers to get the wording changed, but
her suggestions were met with strict instructions to read
the copy exactly.

Tsuneishi arrived before Iva went into the broadcast
booth, and Mitsushio made a point of explaining to the
army commander how Iva wanted changes. Tsuneishi
turned to Iva. "I am sure there is no problem with the script
as written, especially given the generous raise just granted."
The major smiled.

In the booth, Iva swallowed hard, feeling boxed into a
corner. Cousens wouldn't have allowed this situation, and
with the major aware of the copy issue, Iva felt pressured to
read the script as written. What would the Australian do in
this situation? Her mind couldn't seem to focus on what to
do. What did Dr. Amano say about lack of food affecting
the ability to think?

There was her signal. "Hello, boneheads. It's me, Orphan
Ann of the Pacific..."

CHAPTER 16

The next day at the Danish Ministry, Iva worried about possibly having read the propaganda about lost American ships when she knew that wasn't true. Hopefully such an obvious lie would be apparent to anyone listening. It reaffirmed that she needed to get out of Radio Tokyo as soon as possible. She planned to not report to the radio station later that day and accept the consequences whatever they might be.

Sitting at her desk, Iva heard footsteps and turned to see Tillitse standing behind her.

"Sorry, Iva. I hope I didn't startle you, but you seemed so lost in thought. Anything I might help with?"

"It's nothing unusual and everything at once. Why did I get stuck here and have to struggle to stay loyal to my country? Why can't the Japanese accept I'm American and not harass me all the time? I wish this war was over and we could all go home."

"I know how you feel, although my war may be over sooner than the one in this ocean. The Germans are on the run, and my country will soon be rid of the Nazis. Once the previous government is reinstated, I will most likely be called home."

"I never thought about that. Will you be okay?"

"It should be fine. I was the minister for the previous government and only holding down things here during the war. There may be some consequences, since the Germans tried to make it appear under their occupation that Denmark was an ally of Japan. I'll have to deal with that when the time comes."

Iva never realized this kind and generous man might also be a victim of being in the wrong place at the wrong time. Was anything ever fair in a time of war?

Tillitse said, "Iva, I've had a thought. Why don't you join me this weekend at my country house? We can grab some stuff from the pantry and enjoy a quiet weekend with no bombing raids. Just us friends taking a break. Would Filipe understand?"

With the stress of Radio Tokyo that had been building, a couple of quiet days away sounded heavenly to Iva. That might give her time to sort out how to deal with her broadcasting job as well as what to do about a marriage proposal that appeared imminent. She wasn't telling anyone, but she and Filipe had moved out of Maria's house and were sharing an apartment. They came to this decision because the long commute was wearing them both down. Iva surprised herself by how easily she agreed to this new living arrangement, but given the sudden availability of an affordable apartment, it made sense.

Looking across the table at Tillitse, Iva knew he was an honorable man and was sure nothing untoward would be expected on the weekend away. It was a given that Filipe wouldn't be happy, but there was so little she did for herself.

"That sounds wonderful. What can I bring?"

"You pack whatever food you think we need. Be sure to include a bottle of sake. My car has lots of charcoal. It will be a stinky ride, but we'll get there."

ALTHOUGH NEW YEAR'S WAS A MAJOR HOLIDAY ON THE Japanese calendar, the celebrations ringing in 1945 were spartan. Iva and Filipe traveled to spend the holiday with Maria. Now that they were living apart from her, Maria bustled about, showing what she planned for their special evening. The shortages and continued damage from the Allied bombings cast a pall over the country, but as Iva looked at the food the three managed to collect, she knew they were fortunate. Maria had even managed to get three tangerines.

Iva breathed a sigh of relief as she took in everyone's good mood. Filipe was finally over being upset about her weekend away. It helped that Maria had assured her son that nothing was going on between Iva and the minister. Another reason for the celebration was that Iva's weight was up to 85 pounds from a recent low of 72 pounds. It was a ways to go from the 118 pounds she had weighed when she left the United States but probably the best she could do for now.

While Maria prepared dinner, Filipe suggested that he and Iva take a walk. Spying a sideways look from mother to son, Iva thought, *This is it. In the next few minutes, I'll have to commit to this man or permanently damage our relationship. With us now sharing the apartment, aren't we essentially married? I know marriage is the ultimate commitment in life. After the war, it will be the two of us returning to America to be with my family. Fil once said he eventually wants to settle in Portugal. I'll have to convince him his plan won't work, but what about my family? What will they think if I return home married? Will they like Fil? I always thought my family would be around me when I got married. Maybe that will not be in the cards.*

Taking Iva by the arm, Filipe led her outside where the sun was setting. For once, it wasn't unbearably cold. They walked arm in arm as Iva wondered if she was supposed to say something. Wishing he would break the silence, she stopped and turned to embrace him.

He whispered, "We've danced around this enough. You know I want to get married. Please say yes."

Burying her head into his shoulder, Iva heard herself say, "Yes, Fil, yes."

Filipe pulled her closer. "You've made me so happy. Come on, let's get back and tell my mother the good news."

Guess I'm getting married. Am I happy? I think I am.

CHAPTER 17
1945

I n the back of St. Sophia Church, Iva, Filipe, and Maria watched the conclusion of a funeral. Pulling her coat more tightly about her, Iva looked at what was once a beautiful Catholic church now severely damaged by the impacts of war. Several pews were missing, probably taken for firewood, while loose rubble lay all about. In several of the naves, families who lost their homes to the bombing squatted. What would happen to those people if a stray explosive struck the church? Would it be better to die in the house of the Lord?

The ceremony was wrapping up, and while all funerals were tragic, today a child was being buried, which deepened the family's suffering. Once the parents and mourners streamed past her, the three observers stepped forward. The priest had the casket open and was lifting the dead child out of the coffin.

Maria asked, "Father Kraus, what are you doing?"

The tall German priest sighed. "Another sign of the times. There's not enough wood for caskets, so we only rent them for the funeral. This poor soul and others will no longer have that comfort for eternity. Let me take him back for wrapping, and I'll be back in a moment for a happier ceremony."

Iva closed her eyes and wondered how her baptism today and wedding tomorrow could be termed "happy" considering the dire conditions all around them. Only a month before, the Allies conducted two days of a saturation firebombing of Tokyo that resulted in over one hundred thousand deaths. Even now, it was impossible to walk outside without being assaulted by the smell of burning death. Bodies remained in the rubble from that raid and subsequent bombing. Fortunately, after those two horrific days, the Allies were no longer using incendiary bombs.

Signs of more breakdowns in Japanese society were everywhere. The streetcars no longer had seats with coverings, as the leather had been cut away to make clothes. Groups of teenagers wandered the streets as more young Japanese refused to report for work at factories turning out war materials. While they were walking to the church that morning, Iva watched a man fighting to crawl out a window with a desperate woman clutching and screaming that he was stealing her food. Filipe chased the man but was unable to catch him. All around them, people walked the streets resembling ghosts more than humans.

That same despair had been apparent in the staff at Radio Tokyo. The week before, a special messenger had arrived at Iva's apartment, telling her she was to report to work immediately. Despite her claim of an ear infection, the soldier insisted she come with him right then. Once at the radio station, Iva found an angry Oki waiting for her. June Suyama was sitting in the corner of his office.

"The major's whore is finally back at work, although he's not here now to protect you. He has given us additional duties, so George and I will be managing you directly from now on. As of today, you will not miss work, do you understand?"

Iva had looked straight ahead and said nothing.

"Answer me, American. Are you proud of your countrymen firebombing our women and children? You always made it clear how you wanted America to win the war, so are you enjoying the suffering? My wife and children cry every day because they are so hungry. Does that make you happy, American?"

Oki was walking back and forth and getting more agitated. It was clear to Iva there was no reasoning with him, while over in the corner, June was smiling, enjoying the drama.

Iva said, "Okay, I promise to show up to work even if I'm sick and there's bombing." She got up and walked away.

As she left Oki's office, trying to control her temper, she had seen that a good portion of the office had been listening. Ignoring their stares, she headed to her desk. Off to the side, she had heard one of the male announcers say, "She doesn't look so proud now. Good."

Returning to the present, Iva looked up and saw Father Kraus coming back. Looking at Filipe and Maria, she forced a smile. The baptism would make her a Catholic. The Portuguese embassy required a Catholic wedding to recognize the marriage, so Iva agreed to convert even though she doubted ever wanting the option of being a citizen of Portugal. Filipe and Maria were insistent about Portugal recognizing their union, so there she was. Iva's one wish was that Charles Cousens could be here today, but he had recently moved to another prison camp, and no one knew where he was.

Father Kraus said, "If we're ready, let's begin." The air raid sirens started to wail. Smiling, the elderly priest picked up his bottle of water and said, "Guess we can complete this ceremony down in the bomb shelter."

WORK AT RADIO TOKYO STAYED STRESSFUL, BUT OVER time, Iva worked up the courage to skip days again. This time the expected pushback from her two managers didn't develop. When she did broadcast, there was a struggle to keep what she said on air general and not related to the war. Adopting one of Cousens' tricks, she dug out old scripts and read them, ignoring current copy. There seemed less interest in what she was doing at the radio station, since the war continued to wear everyone down.

Another difficult development occurred with her other job. Tillitse's government called him home, and the Ministry in Tokyo was closing. Saying goodbye to the man who had taken her in and been so supportive was particularly emotional, since neither knew what fate awaited him. He was generous to the end and let Iva empty the pantry of food and medical supplies. *I lose Cousens and now this wonderful man. What will happen to me next?*

A further bellwether of the changing times was that a new police representative was assigned to monitor her. In an amazing coincidence, Katsuo Kido, the son of their current landlady, was given the assignment. Much to Iva's surprise, Kido wasn't interested in harassing her. Instead, he wanted to use their meetings to learn about America and work on his English.

As her new police representative explained, "Soon the war will be over, and American troops will rule our country. I need to know how to talk to your soldiers, so please help me prepare for what is coming."

One day at Radio Tokyo, several of the announcers were gathered and laughing. Sticking her head in, Iva asked what was going on.

Ruth Hayakawa turned. "It's a new report explaining how the Americans love our female announcers and have come to call them Tokyo Rose. We're arguing about which one of us is the real Tokyo Rose, although everyone here knows only I can be that person because of the seductive voice I use in my broadcasts."

"You call your whimpering seductive. I call it passing gas," June Suyama said with a smirk. "If anyone is the seductive one, it must be me. I will tell you that the one person who couldn't be Tokyo Rose is Iva. With her terrible voice and lack of talent, she can be broadcasting only because she is sleeping with the major."

After Suyama's comment, the group grew quiet and started to break up. When only Suyama remained to stare at Iva, the American knew this was the person who was writing vicious notes and playing dirty tricks. Ruth had said on that first day that Suyama was a viper.

Iva thought about reacting, but what did it matter anymore? The war would soon be over, and Suyama would be the one suffering. Iva turned and walked away.

Toward the end of June, when Iva reported to the radio station, Mitsushio was waiting for her. She was led into his office. "Iva, things are getting worse because of the war, and I don't think it's safe for you to be here anymore. Many people are angry and scared, and there's a lot of talk about the American traitor in our midst. I think it's best if you get your things, slip out quietly, and don't come back."

Iva's heart beat fast as she realized this terrible chapter at Radio Tokyo was finally at an end. Looking at her boss, she could see he wasn't angry and was doing this out of concern for her safety. Struggling with what to say, she blurted, "Goodbye, and thank you."

On Iva's way out with her few personal possessions, Ruth Hayakawa called and came running down the hall. "I heard they were going to tell you not to come back, so this is goodbye."

Iva looked at the one real friend she had at Radio Tokyo and said, "I guess the war will soon be over, and I hope you'll be okay when that happens."

"You too, and I wish that you get back to America soon. I'll be fine here even though the government's new campaign to train every person to fight to the death with sticks and rocks if the Americans invade scares me."

"Me too. Hopefully Japan will surrender, and it won't get to that."

"We can pray for that. I want to say how much I admire your loyalty to your country and how you refused to do any propaganda. None of the other characters around here have that much backbone. There's one thing I want you to remember. I must be Tokyo Rose, because I'm the most seductive one here."

Iva laughed and reached out to embrace Ruth. "Thanks for everything you did to help me. Take care of yourself." With tears in her eyes, Iva turned and headed out.

Stepping out into the sunlight, Iva saw lines of older women and young girls drilling with sharpened sticks. The joy of being out of Radio Tokyo disappeared as dread overwhelmed her. As Ruth had said, if the Americans did invade and all citizens followed government orders to fight to the death, how would she and Filipe survive? Iva felt so weary that she wondered if she had the energy to take another step.

TRYING TO STAY COOL THROUGH ANOTHER HOT, HUMID August day, Iva contemplated the latest announcement from the Japanese government. All Japanese were ordered to be at a radio to listen to a broadcast from the emperor the following day at noon. The entire country was on edge. What could be so important? No one had ever heard "The Sacred Crane" speak publicly.

With the recent atomic bombings of Hiroshima and Nagasaki, it was obvious the Americans had a new and terrifying weapon. Though suspecting tomorrow might bring an announcement ending the war, Iva tried not to get her hopes up. It was just over four years since she arrived in similar sultry weather, and with the many disappointments over that time, she hoped this was not another setback.

Thinking of her family back in the States, Iva guessed an announcement ending the war would be different there. Hopefully it would mean interned Japanese Americans would be released. Here, what might it mean for her marriage? Now that the knot was tied, Filipe was hardening his position about not moving to America. Last night he said to her, "I'm okay with an extended visit to the States, but I want to live in Portugal. Remember, you have to fill out only one piece of paper to become a Portuguese citizen."

The first time Iva heard this, she said nothing, but now they were often arguing about Iva's commitment to living in the United States.

The following day at noon, sirens across Japan wailed and then were silent as the radio broadcast began. Huddled around an old radio with their landlady and her son, Iva and Filipe heard a scratchy voice speaking in halting phrases, announcing the surrender of Japan. A variety of emotions flooded her as she heard the emperor's words. *Finally it's over. I survived. Now what? How soon before I can get home, especially since I don't have any money? What does this mean for my family? How long before they get released? Tonight there will be another knockdown and drag out with Fil over Portugal.*

Looking out her landlady's open door, Iva saw some neighbors standing at attention as they listened. Once the announcement was over, it was deathly quiet. The silence was soon broken by sporadic cries of anguish from residents in the neighborhood.

Katsuo stood and bowed to Iva. "Congratulations. Your country has won, and they should be proud of you for never bending in your loyalty. You never bought one war bond no matter how much pressure the government applied. My mother and I admire you."

"Thank you, Katsuo. Both of you have been so good to Filipe and me, and we're likely to be here for a while until I figure out how to get back to the United States."

As she said those words, out of the corner of her eye she saw Filipe bristle.

"One last thing," Katsuo said. "There will be a lot of angry and upset people after today's announcement. I encourage you not to celebrate openly and to stay out of sight until things settle down."

BOOK TWO

CHAPTER 18
US OFFICE OF WAR INFORMATION, WASHINGTON, DC
AUGUST 7, 1945

"So that's it? Your investigation into the identity of Tokyo Rose concludes there is no actual character with that name. Instead, there were several female announcers for Radio Tokyo, and none of them openly used that handle. Our servicemen used that title generally for any of those announcers. Is that correct?"

"That's right, Colonel. Tokyo Rose is a figment of the imagination of our guys. Some evidence also points to the female announcers at the Japanese radio station in Manila that our boys heard. No one knows for sure."

Colonel Stevens dropped the investigation report on his desk and chuckled. "It's interesting the navy issued a citation commending Tokyo Rose for her entertaining program. Listen to what the navy wrote: 'In recognition of her morale-building efforts, Tokyo Rose is hereby cited. Tokyo Rose has persistently entertained US Armed Forces during long nights in fox holes and onboard ships, bringing them excellent music, laughter, and news from home.

These broadcasts inspired American servicemen to a greater determination than ever to get the war over quickly so that soon they could thank Tokyo Rose in person."

"Guess the navy will be searching for an individual to thank for a long time. In the meantime, Colonel, what do you want me to do with this report?"

"No one will ever care about this finding, so file it. The deeper you bury it the better."

CHAPTER 19
1945-1946

A week later, Iva and Filipe watched the first American troops move into the Tokyo area. Preceding the arrival of soldiers were wild rumors that all women and children should stay hidden when the Americans arrived because of the rape and random killings sure to follow. Watching jeeps and trucks filled with Americans soldiers drive by, Iva wanted to jump out, shout for joy, and ask to be put on the next ship back to the United States. Between the anger simmering below the surface with most native Japanese and Filipe's resistance about moving permanently to America, Iva kept these thoughts in check.

After the military convoy passed, Iva and Filipe walked home. "There's been no violence that I've heard of," Filipe said. "That's positive."

Iva looked over at him. "The emperor made it clear that all Japanese are to cooperate and obey the American military, so maybe it will stay that way. I wonder what the Americans will do with the emperor."

"I bet they leave him alone. After all, as long as he is telling everyone to cooperate, why touch him?"

"There's something wrong with that. The emperor starts a major war and then avoids any punishment?"

Filipe shrugged and said nothing. As they approached their apartment building, they could see their landlady talking to a stranger and pointing toward them. When they got to the house, the stranger came up and looked directly at Iva. "I'm trying to find Iva Toguri. Is that you?"

Bristling, Filipe stepped forward. "This is Iva D'Aquino, my wife. Who are you, and what do you want with her?"

"My sincere apologies. My name is Leslie Nakashima, and I'm working with two American war correspondents who would like to interview Iva about her time here in Japan and the work she did at Radio Tokyo."

Iva's heart soared. Already there were Americans who knew about her being stuck here and wanted to talk about her experiences.

"My wife doesn't do interviews. We need to know more about who these correspondents are and what they want to talk about."

Iva's anger was immediate. *Who is Filipe or anyone to dictate what I will or will not do? He's probably acting this way because of his resistance to my insisting we go to America as soon as possible. I need to put him in his place.*

Before she could say a word, Nakashima spoke. "They're willing to pay $2,000 for an interview."

Her head swam. That much money would solve their money woes and mean she had the funds to book passage home. She knew her family wouldn't have the resources to pay for her transit, so here was the solution.

Filipe started to speak, but Iva interrupted, ignoring the angry look her husband gave her. "I'll do the interview.

When do they want to meet?"

"They're staying at the Imperial Hotel and would like to meet at one o'clock tomorrow afternoon. Go to the desk and ask for Harry Brundidge and Clark Lee. I'll also be there, and glad this will work for you."

Nakashima started to walk away when Filipe called out to him. "How did you find Iva, and why do they want to talk to her?"

Nakashima turned. "I worked with Clark in Hawaii, which is my home. When Clark got here, he asked me to talk to people at Radio Tokyo. I met there this morning with Kenkichi Oki, who explained that Iva was the person they wanted. These reporters want to do a story on Tokyo Rose and her broadcasts, and Oki said that Iva was Tokyo Rose."

Iva was shocked to hear this. *Why would Oki say I am Tokyo Rose when Ruth made it clear she wanted to be that person? What does it matter if it means $2,000 for us? Besides getting to the United States soon, I'll probably have enough money to help my dad start another business. Uh oh, look at Fil's face. We're going to have a lot of arguing tonight.*

THE NEXT MORNING, IVA AND FILIPE WENT EARLY TO the countryside to forage for food. With uncertainty about the role of the existing Japanese government until the American occupation forces fully took over, most residents were expecting things to get worse before they got better. The supplies she received from the Danish Ministry were long gone, and like everyone else, she and Filipe were struggling from one meal to the next. Until she got that $2,000, trips like this would have to continue.

In their search for food, they had to walk farther than usual. Not only did the farmers seem to have less, but the competition was greater, as many others prepared for the unknown of enemy occupation. With her newly swollen legs and lack of energy from not eating enough, Iva prayed this would be the last time they had to make this trip. After repeated failures to find anything, Iva forced Filipe to hide while she approached a farmer, pretending to be a single mother seeking food for her children. Filipe's ego was clearly bruised when Iva returned with the food.

On the stop-and-start train ride back to Tokyo, the argument Iva and Filipe started the evening before continued. "Look, Iva, I've said it before, and I'll say it again. I don't feel good about this interview. Who are these correspondents, and more importantly, why did Oki identify you as Tokyo Rose? He was never a friend of yours at the radio station. If this interview is such a good opportunity, why didn't he say his wife was Tokyo Rose? Didn't Ruth Hayakawa tell you that if anyone was Tokyo Rose, she was?"

Here we go again. My husband treats me like a child. I've done well surviving in this country and making my own decisions. He's acting like a typical Japanese male and thinking women don't have minds of their own. From now on, I'm making my own decisions, and the heck with him.

"Stop, Fil. I'm tired of this argument, especially since your concern is likely about not wanting me to get $2,000 and being able to get back to the United States sooner rather than later. I've done nothing wrong since I've been here, and I did well before I met you. If someone wants to give me money for being Tokyo Rose, why shouldn't I take it?"

Filipe's anger flared. "I'm not expressing my concern because I don't want you to be able to get back to the United States. I'm concerned that you might get in a situation where something bad could happen. It's not fair of you to think my intentions are anything but for your good and safety."

"All right. Look, I'm doing the interview, and you'll see everything will be okay."

They gave each other a long look, faced forward, and said nothing more.

WHEN THEY ARRIVED AT THE IMPERIAL HOTEL, IVA AND Filipe went to a meeting room in the one wing of the hotel that had no bomb damage. As they opened the door to the meeting room, two Americans and Nakashima were waiting there. The Hawaiian rose and introduced Iva and Filipe to Harry Brundidge and Clark Lee. Both reporters wore US army uniforms. After shaking hands, they guided Iva to a chair on the other side of the table.

"Filipe," Nakashima said, "since Iva is the one to tell her story, you and I can sit over here out of the way."

Iva moved to her seat and sat down while taking in the Americans. Brundidge explained that he worked for *Cosmopolitan* magazine. Previously he had written for the *St. Louis Star-Times,* where he broke some big kidnapping story that he felt the need to explain. He was in his forties with a red face, bushy mustache, and full paunch, and his uniform looked like he'd worn it for weeks. His clothes were still much better than what she'd seen in Japan over the past four years.

Across the table in front of a typewriter was Clark Lee, who explained that he worked for the International News Service. He looked much younger than his partner, but Iva later learned he was also in his forties. Almost a full head shorter than Brundidge, Lee's trim figure contributed to his youthful look. As he wore a big grin, Iva thought he might be a fun person to know.

"If you're ready, Iva, I've got a contract that will pay you $2,000 for today's interview. I want you to read it and sign it before we begin," Brundidge said, "but before I give it to you, I have a question. Are you Iva Toguri, and how old are you?"

Iva was surprised by the question. "Yes, I'm that person, and I'm twenty-nine. Why do you ask?"

"Well, you look like a teenager with those pigtails and how small you are. I want to be sure we're dealing with the right person."

Iva laughed at the well-fed Americans. "If you'd been here for the past years scrounging for food, you'd also be thin. As far as the pigtails, that's the style I like. Is that an issue?"

"No problem. Sorry I asked. Here's the contract, and it's only one page. Take a look and let me know if there are any questions."

Iva took the document and started to read. The words in the first paragraph surprised her. It named her as Tokyo Rose. In the second paragraph, it went further, calling her the one and original Tokyo Rose. The third paragraph specified Iva had no female assistants or substitutes. The remainder of the documents indicated the rights from the interview belonged exclusively to *Cosmopolitan*.

Iva knew Filipe wouldn't like this specific language about her being the one and only Tokyo Rose, but she desperately wanted the money. Besides, what could be wrong about being identified as Tokyo Rose? After a moment of thinking, Iva said, "There's an issue here. There were many female announcers, and none of us were specifically known as Tokyo Rose."

Before handing the contract back to Brundidge, Lee looked at the offending language. "You had no assistants, so that should not be a problem. An original cannot have a substitute, so I think that should eliminate that concern. As an original, you're the only one, so I think this is okay for you to sign. We understand there were other female announcers."

Iva felt confused as the contract was handed back to her. He said this was okay and understood about her not being the only female announcer for Radio Tokyo. She stared at the document, not wanting to make eye contact with Filipe across the room. *I told him I'd make my own decisions, but I'm confused by what the reporter just said. Best to sign this and clarify anything in the future.* She signed "Iva Toguri," not bothering to add her married name, and pushed the document back across the table.

Brundidge gave his fellow reporter a wink and smile. "Good. Let's get started. Clark's going to ask the questions and transcribe your answers using his typewriter. I'll be listening and having a bourbon or two. Anyone else want a drink before we get started?"

Everyone said no, so Clark said, "For the record, could you please state your full name?"

FOUR HOURS LATER, BRUNDIDGE AND LEE ANNOUNCED the interview was complete. Lee had seventeen double-spaced pages that he handed to Iva for review. Iva was exhausted and had a splitting headache. She desperately wanted to get out of the room, so she started to give the transcript a cursory review. Realizing she was not going to read every word, she looked up at Lee and said, "This is fine."

"Good," the reporter said. "At the bottom of the last page, sign your name and also sign Tokyo Rose."

Iva did as she told. "When will I get my money?"

Brundidge, who was well into his cups by now, said, "I don't have it today. I'll wire the contract to my publisher, and I should have the money in a few days. Is that okay with you?"

"I guess so. The sooner we get the money the better."

After Filipe, Nakashima, and Brundidge signed the document as witnesses, Iva and Filipe started to head out the door. Iva heard Lee ask Brundidge, "Did you get what you wanted?"

Brundidge said, "It's hard to believe she could be Tokyo Rose given how late she started working at Radio Tokyo, but that'll do for our purposes of getting the first exclusive about Tokyo Rose."

ON THE STREETCAR HOME, FELIPE ASKED IVA, "DID YOU read every word of that transcript?"

Looking exasperated with her husband, Iva said, "No, but those reporters are American and wouldn't do anything to hurt a fellow countryman. Besides, did you before you signed as a witness?"

"I signed because I assumed you read everything, and with you saying you wanted to get out of there because you were so exhausted, I didn't want to take more time."

"So neither of us read every word. It'll be fine. You worry too much, Fil."

THE NEXT DAY, IVA WAS PREPARING DINNER OVER THEIR small stove when she heard a knock at the door. After the second set of knocks, she ran to the door. Two American soldiers stood there. "Are you Iva Toguri?" the taller one asked.

Iva answered, "Yes. Why? What can I do for you?"

"I'm Sergeant Dale Kramer, and this is Sergeant James Keeney. We're with *Yank Magazine*, a publication of the American military. We want to interview you about your experiences working at Radio Tokyo."

"I already talked with two reporters from *Cosmopolitan* and signed a contract granting them exclusive rights. I have something on the stove and don't want it to burn. Please come in while I take care of that. As in any Japanese home, please remove your shoes."

The soldiers entered the small apartment as Iva hurried back to the stove. Taking the pot off the heat, she turned back to the servicemen. "Back home, my family wouldn't let me cook, but being stuck here, I had to learn. When I get home, it'll be interesting to see if they think I've improved or if the shortage of food here makes everything edible."

Kramer smiled. "I'm sure you're a fine cook. That smells delicious."

"You're too kind. I'd invite you for dinner, but we don't have much."

"That's okay. We know everyone here is struggling to get enough to eat, so we'll have dinner back at our base. In the meantime, you're news, and we'd like to do an interview. You entertained many American service members, and I know they want to hear your story. I believe you said you signed the deal with *Cosmopolitan*, correct?"

"Yes."

"I'm sure that exclusive contract provision doesn't apply to the US government. *Cosmopolitan* is a private publication, so doing an interview with us shouldn't be a problem. As I said, our boys relied on Tokyo Rose for entertainment. They need to hear your story."

Iva glanced at the closed bedroom door, hoping Filipe kept sleeping. It was becoming clear that being labeled Tokyo Rose was going to stick, and as this sergeant said, Tokyo Rose was important to the American war effort. Why not grab some glory along with the interview money? After all she'd suffered, she deserved some reward. Iva smiled. "If you think an interview won't be a problem with the contract, I'd love to share my story. There's much more I'd like to tell you about what happened to me including how I helped POWs in Tokyo."

"Great. How about tomorrow morning for a meeting? Sergeant Keeney can come by and pick you up at ten o'clock. Will that work?"

"Okay. My husband is napping now. I'm sure he'll want to come along. Is that okay?"

"Sure, the more the merrier. We'll get out of your hair so that you can finish your dinner," Kramer said. After extending their hands, the soldiers headed out the door.

After reaching their jeep, Keeney turned to his partner. "Do you think an interview with our magazine won't violate *Cosmopolitan*'s exclusivity clause?"

"Hell if I know," Kramer said. "Look, I was going to say whatever it took to get this interview. Besides the emperor, Tokyo Rose is the most interesting character people want to read about. I'm sure she already got her money, so let the magazine sue her if they choose."

When Filipe returned home and heard about the *Yank* interview, he raised concerns about violating the exclusivity clause. He wasn't so accepting about Sergeant Kramer's justification of *Yank* being exempt as a government publication, and when he asked Iva if she'd gotten Kramer's assurance in writing, they had another fight.

"The Americans are my people and wouldn't do anything to hurt me," she shouted at her husband.

Filipe threw his hands up in frustration. "All right. This is your deal. From now on, I'll keep my mouth shut." He spun and left the room.

THE SUN WAS SHINING, AND IVA ENJOYED THE FEELING OF the wind blowing through her hair as the American army jeep flew down the road. The *Yank* interview that morning had been relaxing and fun compared to the grilling by Lee. She got to tell her entire story including working with Cousens and getting supplies smuggled into the prison camp. Now Iva was on the way to an afternoon press conference, since there were so many other members of the press who wanted access. By doing one group interview, she could avoid being repeatedly bothered. Iva again raised the exclusivity concern, since private publications would be present. Kramer dismissed that issue, saying that by now *Cosmopolitan* had a day's lead and would have gotten their feature out.

Things are heading in the right direction after all the war years, just like I imagined them. Talking to other Americans and seeing some benefit for all I sacrificed over the years makes me happy. Even Fil seems to be forgetting our fight and enjoying the ride to Yokohama. Iva reached over and took her husband's hand. Filipe squeezed her back and gave her a small smile as they headed to an afternoon press conference.

OPENING THE PRESS CONFERENCE WITH THE SAME words she used in the *Yank* interview, Iva said, "If I'm Tokyo Rose, which it seems I am..." Over one hundred correspondents hung on her every word.

When it came time for questions, an Australian reporter stood up. "You don't seem to have the silken voice the soldiers and sailors said they heard telling them their wives and girlfriends were untrue. Was your voice modified in the Japanese broadcasts?"

"My voice was never modified, and I never said anything like that. My job was only to introduce records and make a few general comments. There were lots of female announcers at Radio Tokyo. Maybe some of them said things like that."

Someone suggested that Iva sit in front a microphone to simulate a broadcast, and she was happy to comply. As she smiled and posed, Iva was sure the flashbulbs might mean that her family back in the States would see her image.

After the press conference, Filipe mentioned to Iva that Oki was in the room and had said he wished he'd identified his wife as Tokyo Rose. It was apparent Iva was becoming a hero and would be able to reap the rewards for entertaining Allied troops.

The couple started to look for Kramer so they could get back to Tokyo when another soldier approached, saying Brigadier General Elliot Thorpe wished to talk to Iva but wouldn't be available until the morning. The General wanted them to stay the night as his guest at the hotel used by the US military, and Kramer knew of this change in plans. Iva and Filipe looked at each other and quickly agreed.

That night, they had dinner in the hotel restaurant. They were thrilled, especially since the food kept coming. After dinner, Iva and Filipe headed to their room. A large American MP stood outside their door. "I'm here for security so that no one will bother you," he said.

Iva and Filipe smiled at each other as they settled in, more than happy with the events of the day. "Look, Fil, we had a wonderful dinner with all we could eat. Now we have a free night in this beautiful hotel room, and tomorrow we meet an American general. How much better could things get?"

"It's pretty nice," Fil said. "Do you want anything?"

Iva thought a moment. "Maybe some ice for our water."

"Okay." Filipe went to the door. He twisted the doorknob and asked, "Why is this door secured from the outside?" Banging on the door, he loudly asked, "Guard, why is this door locked?"

The couple heard through the door, "Security, sir. In the morning, I will unlock it. Goodnight, sir."

All the goodwill from the day evaporated. Iva looked at her angry husband and shrugged. "Forget it, Fil. Let's get some sleep."

CHAPTER 20

The next morning, the D'Aquinos were taken to breakfast, where an MP stood close by. At precisely 8:00, Iva was informed that she would be questioned alone by counterintelligence officers, and Filipe could return to their hotel room. This occurred as the couple was leaving the restaurant, so there was no chance for Iva and Filipe to talk. It was clear as they parted that Filipe was extremely upset.

As Iva entered the meeting room, she was introduced to Lieutenant Colonel Benjamin Turner and four other American officers. "I thought I was supposed to be meeting with a general and then heading home," Iva said as she sat down.

"Nothing to worry about," Turner said. "We have a few questions about your time here. It shouldn't take but a few minutes, and then we'll see about meeting with the general."

Iva didn't see one smiling face among the officers. The interrogation began, but after a few minutes, she concluded they weren't asking anything serious. An hour later, Turner turned to his fellow officers and announced, "I see nothing here of interest with this minor case. I suggest we turn this over to Sergeant Page to document Mrs. D'Aquino's story."

The officers left and were replaced by a sergeant who started again from the beginning of Iva's story but delved into greater detail about her experiences. The second interview stretched into the early afternoon, so sandwiches were brought in at lunchtime. Her interrogator assured Iva that Filipe was being fed.

Feeling relaxed with the easy manner of her interrogation, Iva enjoyed the wonderful American roast beef sandwich that she dreamed of many times during the past four years. The atmosphere was further lightened by a parade of officers and soldiers who came to have their pictures taken with Tokyo Rose. More than one left with an autograph reading, "Tokyo Rose, Iva Toguri." One general who stopped by to get an autograph asked if the package of records he ordered dropped from a bomber for her ever made it to the radio station. Iva wasn't sure what to say to this enthusiastic man who would think a package of fragile records dropped in a bombing raid and addressed in English would survive, never mind being delivered. Smiling, she said, "Sorry but no. Thanks for trying."

Later in the afternoon, Sergeant Page took Iva to another room for fingerprinting. Colonel Turner returned and said that the army wasn't able to document whether she was Portuguese or American but would follow up with the State Department. If she was American, there was a possibility that she might be arrested. In the meantime, they said she was free to go and her husband was waiting outside.

Stunned, Iva wondered what had just happened. Everyone was so friendly, and nothing seemed out of sorts. Why might she be arrested, and why wasn't it clear she was American and not Portuguese? When she tried to ask for clarification, the colonel spun on his heels and left her alone.

Getting to the jeep where Filipe was waiting, she saw a grim look on his face. Taking a newspaper from under his arm, he handed her a copy of the *Los Angeles Examiner* from a couple of days before. The headline read "Traitor's Pay." The byline was "Clark Lee."

CHAPTER 21

F ilipe was at work when there was a knock on the door. *Great,* Iva thought, *what can go wrong now?* Earlier that day, a letter from Brundidge arrived, indicating that she had violated the exclusivity clause of the contract and wouldn't be paid. A couple days earlier, Filipe had run into Oki, and he reported that *Cosmopolitan* told Brundidge after the interview that he wasn't authorized to make that payment. Brundidge's only option was to argue that when Iva gave additional interviews, the contract was null and void. Now that had happened. The loss of the money she had counted on crushed her, and she hoped whoever was at the door didn't bring more bad news.

Opening the door, Iva saw two MPs looking down at her. "Are you Iva Toguri?"

"Yes. Why?"

"You're under arrest. Please get your coat, and you may want to grab a toothbrush. You will likely be with us a couple of days."

Iva felt her stomach fall. "What's this about, and what am I charged with?"

"I cannot answer any questions. Things will be explained

to you when we reach the prison. Now please get your coat and toothbrush."

"My husband is at work. I need to talk to him about this."

"You're coming with us right now. If you don't get the things I suggested, we'll enter your house and handcuff you. Do you understand?"

Filled with panic, Iva said, "Yes. I'll be right back."

MORNING LIGHT CREPT INTO THE SINGLE WINDOW AT the Eighth Army Stockade in Yokohama, and Iva fought to keep her eyes closed as long as possible. Now in her tenth day of imprisonment, despite repeated requests, she had not been allowed contact with Filipe or an attorney. She was subject to daily interrogation sessions with the same questions about why she committed treason. "How did you advise the Japanese government to plan and implement their propaganda program? Is it true that you often dined with the emperor and other top military leaders? Did you plan your trip to Japan knowing the war was coming so you would be in place to work in propaganda?" The questions seemed like Alice in Wonderland at the Mad Hatter's Tea Party. Her interrogators kept repeating how cunning and deceitful she was. Whenever Iva demanded to know the charges against her and how long she would be held, there were no answers.

Just before her arrest, Iva had cooperated with the US military to make two instructional films for the army and navy on how the Japanese conducted their radio broadcasts. In return for being helpful, she was isolated in prison and repeatedly browbeaten.

For the first few days, she was given one bucket of warm water daily to bathe. Iva grew increasingly uncomfortable as she struggled to wash and wear her one set of clothes. After a week, the Red Cross got in to see her and brought additional clothing. The key news the Red Cross representative shared was about the continued stories in the Los Angeles press and calls by the US Attorney in that city for prosecution. That was why the army locked her up. Now the military was trying to figure out if she was guilty of treason. All the Red Cross representative could offer was to carry a message to Filipe.

The prison officials informed Iva that she would soon be transferred to Sugamo Prison where other war criminals were imprisoned. When Iva asked how long she would be there, her interrogator said not to worry, as she was going to be locked up for a long time. She hoped the new prison would eliminate the constant parade of soldiers and their girlfriends from randomly opening the sliding window in her cell and demanding Tokyo Rose autographs. To make them go away, she obliged. At least there had not been a repeat incident of discovering a visiting US congressman observing her when she was allowed a rare shower. When she objected to the prison authorities, they said, "What do you expect as a prisoner?"

How can things get any worse? Here I am held without charges or contact with anyone. Now I learn my case is being driven by press and politics back in Los Angeles. What can I do? I've done nothing but be loyal to my country. What must my family be thinking? My insides ache all the time, and I want this to stop.

Iva heard the panel at the bottom of the cell door slide open, and her breakfast tray was pushed in. "Here's your breakfast, bitch. Be ready to move in an hour when we come back."

———

READING HER BIBLE IN HER NEW PRISON'S SIX-BY-NINE-foot cell, Iva lifted her head to rest her eyes. She was thankful for a text as big as the bible, for this was the only book available she hadn't read several times. This was her third month of captivity, there was still no contact with anyone outside the prison. The daily interrogations had ended with only an occasional follow-up session. Iva was resigned to the lonely and boring routine. She'd given up bothering to ask about the charges against her. Now, three days before Christmas, she remembered how she used to dread the holiday during the war, since it made her so homesick. After all the hope she felt when the war ended, she was in a worse situation and more alone than ever.

Iva heard keys in the door, and when it swung open, there stood Filipe. Jumping up, she flew into his arms, causing one of the bags he was holding to fall to the ground. "Fil," she cried. "At last. How did you manage to get in?"

"Twenty minutes," a voice called from outside the door.

Stepping back, Filipe said, "As you heard, we only have twenty minutes. Three months with no contact and now only a few minutes. Some Christmas present. They told me starting next month I can visit once a month but again only for twenty minutes each time."

Iva started to cry as she hugged him. "What have I done wrong? Why are they treating me like this? I ask them what the charges are, and they say nothing. I ask to see an attorney, and they say that's not possible. The Japanese living under the occupation have more rights than me."

"I know, and no matter how many times I petition to visit you, they send me away without an explanation. I've hired an attorney, although the Americans are stonewalling him too. Anyway, here are some things they let me bring in. This bag has food including fruit I was able to get. There are clothes and a few books for you in the other bag. Since I haven't been able to talk to you, I didn't know what to bring, so before I leave, let me know what you need."

She smiled through her tears. "This is wonderful. Having some different food will be nice, and clothes are a godsend. The stuff the Red Cross brought doesn't fit all that well. Pencils and some paper to write on would be great and maybe a few more books. All I'm reading is the bible."

"I'll bring that. Iva, this cell is terrible. It's so small, and you don't even have a table."

"I have that board in the corner I can put over the sink to make a table, and at least this prison is warm. The Americans have fuel, so that's a blessing." Iva tried to smile bravely.

"Have they given you any documentation? The attorney asked me to bring anything you might have."

She shook her head. "They've given me nothing in writing."

"This is so frustrating. How are you holding up?"

"It's so boring, especially now that they've stopped interrogating me regularly. I'm stuck in this cell all day. My novelty has worn off, so people don't come by anymore to gawk at me as a distraction." Iva decided not to mention the congressman who had spied on her in the shower.

Taking his wife back in his arms, Filipe said, "I wish I knew what more to do. I thought that Tokyo Rose stuff might blow up in your face, but I never thought it would get this bad."

Nuzzling her head in her husband's shoulder, she said, "I hate to say you were right, but I did nothing wrong. I told them over and over there were other women who played Tokyo Rose on the radio. I wish now I'd agreed to have a baby. Maybe that would have kept me out of here."

"Our attorney is guessing the military doesn't know what to do with you. There's pressure back in the United States to prosecute Tokyo Rose, and the authorities think that's you. Some reporters have written wild stories that paint you as a collaborator with the Japanese. Since it's unlikely the army has found any evidence of that, they're just holding you, so we get no information about charges or when you might get out of here."

The same voice came from outside the cell. "Five minutes, you two."

Iva pushed closer to her husband. "I don't want to be alone again. I wish you didn't have to leave."

"Me too, but there's one more thing I have to give you." Stepping back, Filipe reached into his pocket and pulled out a sealed letter. "This was delivered by the Red Cross to our home after your arrest. It's from your brother and written back in '43. Lord knows where it's been sitting all this time. I'm sorry I won't be able to be with you when you read it, since I'm sure there's difficult news given the internment of your family."

Iva's eyes widened as she recognized her brother's handwriting. Controlling herself, she pushed the letter into her pocket and reached again for Filipe. "Hold me until you have to go."

Clinging to each other, they heard the keys in the lock, and the door swung open. "Time's up."

Kissing Iva a final time, Filipe stepped back. "Merry Christmas, Iva. I love you. See you next month."

When her cell door swung shut and she was alone again, she pulled the letter from her pocket. Sitting down on her bed, she gazed at her brother's writing on the envelope. With shaking hands, she gently tore open the letter and read.

Dear Iva, I pray this letter will reach you, since the Red Cross promised to do all they could to find you in Japan. We're all sorry you're stuck there, and I know Dad blames himself every day for not listening to you sooner and getting you home. Hopefully our aunt and uncle are taking good care of you. We all pray for your well-being every day.

News that Japanese Americans are interned might have reached you. We're currently at the Gila River Center in Arizona. June and Inez are here along with my new wife, Miyeko. (I met her shortly after you left, and we got married right before the internment.) We all have jobs in the camp, so that helps pass the time.

Dad got a job buying and securing supplies for all the internment camps, so he travels around the US and mostly Chicago for the actual buying. According to what he has seen at other facilities, he said we're lucky to be at Gila River, since conditions are worse in the other camps.

My sad news is that our mother died after we were required to report. They took us and put us in a horse barn in Tulare near Fresno until they figured out where we'd finally go. You know how ill Mom was when you left, and by the time we had to move, she was also partially paralyzed.

They eventually took Mom to the local hospital, where they allowed one of us to accompany her. June was with her when she passed, but as June said to us later, she died once we were put in that barn.

The last words our mother said to us before going to the hospital was she knew when you got on that ship that would be the last she would see you. Fumi wanted us to tell you how sad she was that you got stuck there but that she was sure her sister was taking good care of you. Our mother loved you, and it broke her heart how things worked out.

I must end this letter, but if this reaches you, perhaps the Red Cross in Japan will get letters from you back to us. Use the return address on the envelope when you write to us. In the meantime, we're hoping you're doing the best you can. As I said, Dad blames himself every day for not listening and getting you home before the war started. No matter how bad things might be here in these camps, we'd prefer you to be with us. Everyone sends their love, Fred.

Iva brought her hands up to her eyes. *My mother's dead. They put her in a horse barn. What's going on in my country? America's supposed to be better than this. My government threw all Japanese Americans in camps during the war, and here they lock me in prison and won't even tell me what the charges are because of politics back home. American reporters I trusted in interviews to tell my story twisted my words and lied about me. We're supposed to be treated fairly in America. How can this be happening?*

Looking down at the letter, Iva wondered where her family was now. She was glad to hear they had been together during the war and in a camp where the conditions were better. Not surprisingly, her father, with his work ethic, managed to be buying supplies and traveling around the country. Leave it to Jun to figure out how to work the system. The news of her mother crushed her. Iva had been dismissive of the ghosts who visited Fumi, but her mother had seen the future, and now she was gone.

Lying back on her bed, she covered her face and sobbed, feeling the worst ache since she had arrived in Japan. *Maybe if I just died, I wouldn't have to suffer anymore. At least then I'd be with my mother. How do I know my family is okay today? Have they been released yet? Are they together? All I have is this letter from years ago. Why is this happening? Oh Mom, how could they do that to you?*

MONTHS ROLLED BY, AND IVA REALIZED SHE WAS COMING up on the first anniversary of her imprisonment. There was still no statement from the prison authorities about charges. The attorney Filipe hired made repeated contacts with occupation authorities and discovered her case was slowly making progress.

When Filipe appeared for his monthly visit, for the first time he brought letters from her family. It was uplifting to finally have regular communication with her family. Rather than having letters sent directly to the prison where authorities would censor them, Filipe had letters sent to him that he smuggled in. In return, Iva slipped her mail back to the United States through her husband so he could post them outside the prison.

It was a relief to know that June and Fred were with her father and working at a new family store in Chicago. Inez had stayed in Arizona and was working to help Japanese

Americans released from camps get settled again. Jun was especially angry to learn about the Hattoris and how they had treated Iva, who would not have needed the job at Radio Tokyo if the Japanese relatives were more caring. None of this trouble would have happened. Her father said Fumi would be ashamed of her sister's behavior. Jun said in each letter that he knew Iva was innocent, and he offered whatever she needed to pay for an attorney and transit to the United States once she was released.

Iva tucked away the stack of letters Filipe gave her. "Any news from our attorney?"

Filipe responded, "The good news is his network is getting better, and information is starting to trickle into him. Just yesterday he learned the Intelligence Branch that interviewed you months ago told the army attorneys there's no basis to bring charges and recommended immediate release. The army attorneys don't want to take responsibility for your release, so they kicked the decision to the Justice Department in Washington. That's why the FBI assigned Agent Tillman to interrogate you last week. Now that he's back in Washington, we have to wait and see what he reports. I assume the session with him went well."

Previously over two days of questioning, the perpetually angry Tillman had been relentless in trying to prove her guilt. "Come on, Iva, how did they force you to do the broadcasts? Did they beat you? Did they put a gun to your head? I don't see how there was any duress."

By the second day, Iva had reached the breaking point. "Please, Agent Tillman, my head hurts, and I need some rest. I can hardly think straight because we've been at this for so long."

"You have a headache because you're guilty. Admit it. You committed treason."

"Why are you being so mean to me and assuming I'm guilty? Isn't it clear I was trapped here and even sacrificed by giving my food to POWs?"

"Don't think that impresses me. I have buddies who died battling the Japanese, and today their children are living without fathers. In the meantime, you're sitting behind a microphone and maybe feeling a little hungry. You should've done nothing to help these bastards."

Starting to cry, Iva had said, "I didn't help them. I did what I was forced to do. Why can't you see that?"

"Don't use the crying routine on me. That won't work. Admit that you like the Japanese and wanted them to win the war. Look, you even married one."

By the end of the interrogation, Iva had been given another transcript to review. Tillman pressured her to review the document and sign her agreement quickly. Through her pounding headache, Iva thought about not fully reading the interview transcript with Brundidge and Lee and how Filipe would be upset if she didn't fully read the document. *I'm so exhausted and cannot focus my eyes, and I need to get away from this place and this awful FBI agent. What's the likelihood that people would not be honest with me twice in a row? I'm going to sign this and be done with him.*

Iva decided not to share how terribly the FBI interrogation had gone, and to possibly open the old wound of not reviewing the transcripts thoroughly. "I'm not sure how it went, Fil, but it sounds like it's more wait and see. The government doesn't appear to think resolving my case is a priority."

"We're doing all we can. Look, our time is almost up. Let me show you what I brought you this month."

As her husband brought out some books and sweets, Iva wanted to cry in frustration but blinked back her tears.

⌐‿⌐

A MONTH LATER, THE TRIM, DARK-HAIRED COMMANDER Hardy visited her. "Iva, I wanted to deliver this news personally. I've been given the go-ahead to release you. We've got some paperwork to do tomorrow, and after that, you can get out of here."

Iva felt her legs almost give way, since she had begun to wonder if this would ever happen. *Why now? I should ask. After all this time, who made the final decision? Better to not say anything and count my blessings.*

"Commander Hardy, what time will I be able to leave?"

"We'll release you at seven o'clock to hold down the press coverage. Filipe was notified, and said he'll be waiting for you outside the prison. We'll have a jeep available and two MPs to drive you home. Tomorrow you can prepare yourself and pack your things. Despite an evening release, I'm sure some press will be outside, and you'll have to deal with them. Let me be clear—no charges are being brought against you."

Iva's heart soared. *They've already alerted Fil and will have transportation for us. That's the least they can do. Of course, there are no charges. Maybe when I meet with the press tomorrow, I can tell them what a fiasco this has been with me rotting here for more than a year.*

The commander said, "Anything I might clarify or help you with right now?"

Iva shook her head, and he was gone. Looking around her tiny cell, she saw it wouldn't take long to pack. *Might as well get started now, because I'm so excited that I doubt I'll sleep much tonight. Over a year spent sitting in this cell, and for what?*

IVA STOOD BY THE MPs WHO CARRIED HER FEW BAGS. On the other side of the door, a large press group awaited. Filipe had been brought in, and she held the bouquet he brought.

"Iva, ready?" Commander Hardy asked.

"More than ready."

The door opened, and Iva and Filipe stepped out into the darkness that was immediately lit by hundreds of exploding flashbulbs. The burly MPs pushed through the crowd of reporters who all shouted questions. Iva realized it was too chaotic to make her planned statement about being a loyal American, and she allowed herself to be shepherded into the back of the jeep.

The jeep quickly left the frustrated reporters behind. Leaning against her husband, Iva whispered so the MPs couldn't hear, "Oh Fil, I've missed you so much. You were my one true friend through the war and during this awful experience. I love you so much and only want to be home with you. Let's go home and think about starting a family."

Filipe pulled her closer. "We're not going home. A friend loaned me his vacation home so we can duck the press until they lose interest. As far as making a family goes, I'm ready for that."

CHAPTER 22
1947-1949

Another Christmas in Japan was approaching. *Will I ever get to have a real American Christmas again?* Iva wondered. Now in her last month of pregnancy, everything was a real effort, but the thought of a baby excited her and helped shift her focus from developments that were keeping her from returning to the United States.

A month after her release from prison, Iva applied for a passport to return home. Filipe still wasn't pleased with the thought of moving to the United States, but Iva wanted her baby to be born in America. Because she was so adamant, Filipe stopped objecting. As the months passed with no word from the US State Department, it became apparent that no passport would come in time for the birth. After repeated visits to the American embassy, Iva was informed there was no record of her citizenship. To move forward, she would have to apply to become a citizen before a passport could be issued.

Iva cried hard that night, realizing that her baby would be born in the country she'd come to hate. *Why does this craziness continue? I was born in the United States. If the State Department gave me that Certificate of Identification*

*when I first traveled here, why do they question my citizen-
ship now? What the State Department is doing has to be
discrimination. As a result, my baby will suffer and not be
born in the States, but I promise myself I will get home one
day, and my child will an American just like I am.*

With renewed determination, Iva started the process
of applying for US citizenship. Besides the birth certificate
provided by her father and original Certificate of Identification, she had to chase down documentation of all her jobs
in Japan and prove she was never a Japanese citizen. With
so many records destroyed at the end of the war, it was a
laborious process. Invaluable help came from her landlady's
son, Katsuo, who did much of the legwork. Once Iva was
able to submit the full application, she was informed there
was a huge backlog and she would not hear for some time
about a final decision.

The cloud of having been identified as Tokyo Rose sur-
faced again when Filipe brought home news that a cartoon
had been released in the United States by a company named
Looney Tunes. The short film parodied Tokyo Rose in the
most racist and treasonous manner possible. "The press
and the public will never let you being that person go," her
husband said, venting his exasperation. "I'm afraid you have
a reputation that will follow you for the rest of your life.
That's why I think it's a good idea we take another look at
you becoming a Portuguese citizen. If we moved there, you
could apply for a visa to travel to America to visit with the
baby. With this crazy State Department application process,
there's no guarantee you'll ever be successful."

Iva stared at her husband. "You want to get me to go
to Portugal one way or another. I'll only be able to visit my

family. What good is it if our child is American but raised in Portugal? I'll never let anything get in the way of getting home permanently. I know what's best for our baby and me."

"I'm only trying to help you with options. When will you see I'm on your side?" In frustration, Filipe grabbed his coat and left the apartment without another word.

Iva banged her hand on the table. *Why do I always find the wrong thing to say to Fil? He's only trying to help and is as excited about the baby as I am. He's even agreed to move permanently to the United States if I get a passport. Can't he see how getting home and living in America again with my family is what I most want? I'm doing the right thing, and he'll have to give up any idea of Portugal.*

―

IVA SQUEEZED HER EYES SHUT AS HARD AS SHE COULD to keep the tears from running freely. She held her lifeless baby in her arms. Filipe sat on the bed with his arm around his wife. In the background, a nurse waited to take the baby away.

I don't want to think or even breathe. Why am I so cursed, and why did this innocent boy have to be part of whatever I'm being punished for? Nothing I touch goes right. Why did I think having a baby would turn things around? Could it be this Japanese hospital caused the death? Would things have been better in an American hospital or a Portuguese hospital? This poor baby. What have I done?

The nurse stepped forward, looking at Filipe.

"It's time, Iva," Filipe whispered.

Reaching down and kissing the lifeless body one more time, Iva turned away as the nurse gently lifted the baby.

Filipe shifted closer and attempted to hold his wife.

"I need to be alone, Fil. I love you, but I need to be alone."

Kissing her one more time, Filipe stood up and left through the privacy curtain. Iva let herself go as her body shook uncontrollably. *Let me die now. It's not worth the struggle anymore.*

CHAPTER 23

Two months later, the American embassy contacted Iva. Representatives of the Justice Department wanted to interview her on March 26. When she asked why, the local State Department representative assured her this was part of the normal process to confirm her citizenship and passport. The employee went on to say, "I probably shouldn't tell you this, but a couple of months ago, the Justice Department indicated it approved a passport for you. I think this interview is to close the loop and finally get things settled."

Iva struggled with depression after losing the baby, and this was the first ray of light. When she mentioned the upcoming interview to Filipe, he asked, "If your government approved you getting a passport a couple of months ago, why haven't you gotten that document yet? Why do they need another interview and go to the trouble of sending somebody from Washington to discuss this? Something doesn't seem right. I think you need to be careful about this meeting. Maybe you should have our attorney present."

Filipe's history of caution and resistance to America ignited Iva. "There you go again, seeing nothing but the worst. The embassy person said my passport was approved, so this is simply to complete the process. Why do I care if the government wants to send people all this way? Maybe it's to apologize. Sometimes you get on my nerves."

Having seen this side of Iva before, Filipe knew better than to argue with her. It so frustrated him that she never recognized some people weren't working in her best interest. *Maybe I'm cautious,* he thought, *but given the way things have gone up to this point, why does she continue to have this blind spot? She throws my preference for Portugal into every argument even though I've said I'll go with her to America if that is what she wants. She can be so frustrating.* Throwing up his hands, he said, "Do you want me to go to the interview with you? I can make arrangements at work, and I'd like to be there in case I can help."

"I'll be fine," she said. "You don't need to come."

———

THE MORNING OF MARCH 26 FOUND IVA HAVING BREAKfast with Earl Carrol, a Broadway and Hollywood producer who had recently contacted her. The meeting with the Justice Department representatives would take place that afternoon. After months of leaving her house only a few times, she now had a full day of meetings. Iva waited for the slightly pudgy producer with big ears to react to the account Iva finished about her years in Japan.

"Iva, your story is amazing, and I think it'd make a terrific Broadway play," Carrol said. "The fact there was more than one Tokyo Rose and how one trapped American got accused of treason while working to sabotage broadcasts and smuggle food and medicine to American POWs—people will eat it up. To make this work, you must assure me you never committed treason. Is that true?"

Iva's spirits soared. A Broadway play would finally tell her story and provide financial support for her and Filipe. It would be everything she could hope for. She still smarted from Brundidge not paying her for his interview, but this play would more than compensate for that. "I can assure you I did nothing wrong, and I have been loyal to the United States. Yes, there were numerous female announcers. I can name those who did propaganda broadcasts. I only introduced and played records."

"Good. That's what I need to hear. Are you aware of what Walter Winchell is saying about you back in the States?"

"No. Winchell is a radio commentator and writes for newspapers, right?"

"Yes. He's one of the most popular news commentators with his Sunday evening broadcast. I've known Walter for years, and he can be unscrupulous at times in creating stories that stoke his popularity. He's trying to do that with you, telling his listeners you committed treason and need to be tried. Given this is an election year, even the president is paying attention, since there's national paranoia about communist infiltration of the government and treason."

Iva sat up. "I'm not a communist."

"I didn't say you were, but Winchell is reporting that what you did in your broadcasts was disloyal to America. The impression many of us have is that he wants to create a controversy to get more people to listen and read his columns."

"People from the Justice Department are meeting with me this afternoon. From what I understand, they'll be giving me a passport, so it can't be that big of a deal."

"That's a good sign. If Justice thought there was a question on the treason front, I doubt they'd be giving you a passport. Still, Winchell is stirring things up. Like I said before, I know him, and when I get back, I'll reach out to him and explain how he's off base with the charges he's making about you. Hopefully it will get him calmed down when I tell him your real story. I must talk to backers for this play and figure out a plan and the timing for developing the script. We'll need you in New York to work with us on that, but once you have your passport, I imagine you'll get back to America as soon as possible."

"Yes. I long to see my family. They went through a lot during the internment."

"That's another example of people overreacting and mob psychology. Well, I'll be in touch, and I'll let you know what Walter says as well as next steps on the play."

As Carrol headed out, Iva tried to process what he had said about Winchell. *Why would someone like him make up stories without talking to me about what actually happened? What is this national paranoia about communism and treason? Could that affect me? Hopefully this afternoon's meeting is only to finalize my passport situation. Most importantly, my luck has finally turned with Mr. Carrol and a play on Broadway.*

IVA WAS WAITING IN THE MEETING ROOM WHEN BRUN-didge and another man walked in. Surprised to see the reporter there, Iva didn't say anything. Brundidge walked over to her and warmly said, "You remember me, don't you?"

Bristling, Iva said, "Yes, I do, but I thought I'd be meet-ing with representatives of the Justice Department, not reporters. Besides, you have the nerve to walk in here after promising me $2,000."

John Hogan stepped forward and introduced himself. "I work directly for the Attorney General, and Mr. Brundidge has been hired to help me with this meeting today."

Hogan stepped back, and Brundidge spoke up. "You violated the exclusivity clause of the contract, so it was out of my hands. It'd be best if we put that aside right now, because the issue today is whether you want your passport or not. You want to go home, right?"

Iva said, "The embassy told me I'd be getting my passport today."

Hogan looked at the reporter as Brundidge continued. "We have a bit of business first. I have here the notes from the interview we did when we first met. Do you recognize them?"

Iva angrily took the notes and started to look at them. Not able to fully focus on reading as her mind raced, she wondered what this was all about. *Why is it important that I read these notes? Is there a possibility I won't be getting my passport today? I can't focus on what is in front of me. I wish Filipe were here. Damn, why did I tell him I'd be fine on my own?* Forcing herself to read as best she could, she looked up and said, "It's been years since we met. I can't be sure these are fully accurate."

"Take another look. I believe these notes reflect the copy you signed with Clark Lee."

Iva tried again to read, but her mind would not focus. This discussion was too confusing. "I don't know if they're accurate. I think there are some things here I didn't say."

Brundidge looked at Hogan and turned back to Iva. "Do you want to return to the United States?"

"Yes, of course."

"Then you need to sign these notes. If you don't agree, there'll be no passport, and you'll die in this godforsaken country."

Iva's eyes widened. *No passport without signing this? Why would someone from the Attorney General's office travel here with Brundidge? What should I do? A lot of this does look familiar, but I can't be sure.*

"Look, Iva," Brundidge said, "we don't have all day. We're leaving in a few minutes. Sign the notes, or resign yourself to a lifetime in Japan."

Iva panicked. If signing this document was necessary to get home, she had to do it. Besides, Carrol was going to take care of her when he got back to New York. How could this be a big deal since it would mean she'd get her passport? Taking the pen Brundidge pushed toward her, she signed her name.

"Got it. We're done here," the reporter said as he handed the document to the Justice Department representative.

Hogan took the signed notes and headed out the door. Brundidge started to gather his things and smiled at Iva. "Thanks. That's good you signed. We lost the original copy."

Iva tried to return his smile. "What's the next step for getting my passport?"

Brundidge looked her in the eye. "You'll be shipped back to the United States shortly to go on trial for treason, so you won't need a passport. After that, probably a short prison sentence, since they'd never hang a woman. See you in America."

CHAPTER 24

"Now that you've read the story Brundidge wrote for that newspaper in Tennessee," Filipe said, "you can see he's already convicted you of treason. You're in real trouble. I'm surprised they haven't arrested you yet. I know you don't want to hear it and always react when I bring it up, but why did you sign those notes? You said you told them there were things you didn't remember, but you went ahead and signed anyway. When are you going to realize people like Brundidge are willing to tell lies if they have an agenda?"

Iva looked down at the copy of the *Tennessean Newspaper*. She knew Filipe was right to be upset with her. *Why do I keep making the same mistake of thinking things will work out if I tell the truth? I'm so focused on getting home that sometimes I don't stop and think. Hopefully none of this will affect Earl Carrol and the Broadway play.*

"Iva, what did you think when you signed that?" Filipe wasn't going to let this go.

"I know I messed up. I should've been more careful. You've been right to warn me, and it isn't fair the way I've reacted with you. I know you love me and have my well-being at heart. I promise to listen more in the future."

"Whatever your future may hold. Just because the army hasn't arrested you doesn't mean it might not happen any day."

"What about Earl Carrol? He said in his cable that he talked to Winchell, and the newsman promised to contact me and hear my story directly. If Winchell understands, he can set the record straight and help me explain why those notes aren't what they seem."

"Has the great Walter Winchell been in touch with you? We'll have to see if he follows up. In the meantime, having your situation all over the news is bringing shame to your family. Just what you want—more national news about Iva."

Iva lowered her head. "In his last letter, my father said he'd stand by me no matter what. He knows I didn't do anything wrong."

Filipe sat down and took his wife in his arms. "I'll be with you no matter what happens."

Iva buried her head in Filipe's chest.

IVA OPENED THE CABLE THAT WAS DELIVERED.

Mrs. D'Aquino, as Earl Carrol's secretary, it is my unfortunate responsibility to inform you that two days ago, Mr. Carroll died in an airplane crash. Your play, as well as all the other projects he was working on, must be terminated. I'm sorry to have to deliver this news to you. Mary Walters

Collapsing on a chair, Iva let the cable drop to the ground. *Does everything I touch go bad? When am I ever going to catch a break? This poor man who perished—why that on top of everything else? Is there anyone out there who can help me?*

ANSWERING THE DOOR, IVA SAW THE SAME TWO BURLY MPs who arrested her once, and here they were again on August 26. Filipe was at work. *Did the government plan it this way?*

This time she was prepared. She went into the bedroom for a bag of clothes and personal items she had packed and quickly wrote a note to Filipe. The guards had said she was heading back to Sugamo Prison. As she stepped out of her apartment, she glanced back, wondering if she'd ever see this home or her husband again.

BOOK THREE

CHAPTER 25

The vibration of the engines on the *General H. F. Hodges* woke Iva, who got up and turned on the light in her small cell in the bowels of the ship. At least there was no mandate to keep the lights on all night because of a concern about suicide. Something as small as being allowed to sleep in the dark was appreciated.

She heard a knock at the door. "It's Kate. I have your breakfast. You ready?" Captain Katherine Stoll of the Women's Army Corps was one of her two female escorts for the return trip home. More importantly, Stoll had become a confidant during the voyage.

"Sure, Kate. Come on in." Iva wrapped herself in her bathrobe.

Stolle placed the breakfast tray on the table. "Mind if I stay a while and give you some company while you eat?"

Iva looked at the food and felt ill. "I'm not sure I can eat that. Probably best to take it with you when you leave, but I'm happy to have you visit."

"We've discussed this, Iva. You've got to eat to keep up your strength. With the dysentery you're battling, you need to replace those lost fluids. Do you need me to get the doctor to see you again?"

Her dysentery had become chronic because of poor diet during the war years. "No, I'll be fine. I never recovered my strength after losing the baby."

Nodding her head sympathetically, Stoll said, "You were skin and bones when I met you, and now you've lost more weight. I wonder if your dress will stay up without pinning."

Iva gave a wry smile. "Who cares? I never get out of this cell, so why even get dressed? You told me it would take twenty-two days to get to San Francisco. All so the government could avoid putting into port in Alaska or Hawaii, since by law I'd have to be tried there. Instead, we're on this endless odyssey so the government can put me ashore in San Francisco where there's strong anti-Japanese sentiment. Is there anything the government won't throw at me?"

"Yes, they're making it as hard for you as possible. As we discussed earlier, it appears all the attorneys at Justice recommended that your case be dismissed because of a lack of evidence, but the Attorney General himself insisted you be charged and tried. Tom Clark is close to President Truman, and he wants his boss to look tough on treason for the election. You're the scapegoat they've settled on."

None of this was new to Iva, but hearing it again made her blood boil. *Winchell and the press are demanding a trial, so the government is going to give them one no matter what the facts are. That national notice issued by the FBI looking for anyone with evidence against me further stacks the deck. My prosecution is all about politics and the heck with the truth.*

Stoll smiled and shook her head. "I checked again this morning, and there's still no word from your home in Japan. The radio operator corralled me later and said this ship is under orders to not accept any messages from Filipe. I'm sorry, but even if your husband is trying, he won't get through."

Another strike against me. Why is the government being so extreme? Trying me for something I didn't do was not enough. Do they want to destroy my marriage too? Iva stayed quiet as she struggled to control her emotions.

Stoll broke the silence. "As I said before, I'm worried about you. It's not just your weight loss and lack of energy, but it looks to me like you've given up. I can see how this is eating away at you. From everything you've told me, you're innocent, but you're going to have to be strong to prove that during your trial. You had the strength and resourcefulness to survive the war years in Japan, and now you need that same energy and fight. Your family is going to want you to win this thing."

"Kate, I'm so tired, and no matter what I do, it ends up falling apart. Now I'm going to be part of a trial that the government is stacking against me and will bring shame to my family. I don't feel like fighting anymore. Look where it's gotten me."

CHAPTER 26

Sitting on the edge of her bunk, Iva tried to smile at Stoll and the other matron, Erma. "Just like you said, Kate, I can't keep my skirt on without these safety pins. I'm not going out there with the press ready to pounce and have my skirt fall off."

"Now that we're in port," Stoll said, "we're under strict orders for no sharp objects on your person. In a few minutes, two FBI agents will be here to take you ashore. They're not going to like this."

"I don't care what they like. The agents will put me in handcuffs and not care if I'm humiliated. I'm not moving until they agree the safety pins stay."

The escorts stepped outside the cell, and Iva heard an animated conversation between the women and what had to be her escorts. With a clear curse, the door swung open, and Frederick Tillman stepped in. "Hello, Iva. Remember me? It's time to go, you treasonous bitch. Get those safety pins off and quit stalling."

Iva looked long and hard at the agent who questioned and mocked her in Japan. Now here he was again and not showing her the slightest respect.

Iva quietly said, "I've lost so much weight that my skirt

falls off when I move. Ask Kate and Erma, and they'll tell you how sick I've been on this trip. You'd like nothing more than to watch me be humiliated in front of the press, but I'm not going to let that happen. I don't move until you agree the safety pins stay."

"If you refuse to move, we'll carry you out. How do you think the press will like that?"

"Probably make for a good picture with two big FBI agents manhandling a small woman." Iva looked over Tillman's shoulder and saw Stoll giving her a thumbs up.

From the corridor, they heard the other agent say, "Come on, Fred, let it go. We're going to handcuff her anyway. Let's get her off this ship and past the press."

Tillman's face went dark. "All right. Keep those damn safety pins in. I haven't forgotten all the soldiers you harmed, and now I have the power over you. Don't you forget that. Let's go."

Stepping into the hallway, Iva embraced her matrons and thanked them for their company and kindness. "Good luck, Iva," Stoll whispered through her tears. "You don't deserve this kind of treatment, and good for you for standing up to that bully."

Iva whispered back, "It feels good for even a small victory like this. Maybe it's time to start fighting again."

The agents pushed Iva forward and up a series of stairways until they walked out on the deck where they put her in handcuffs. The bright sunshine hurt her eyes after so many days below deck. What struck Iva even more forcefully was the mild California weather, something she used to long for. Looking toward the front of the ship, she saw service members rushing down the gangway into throngs of happy families and well-wishers. Ahead of her was an empty gangway where the press waited at the bottom. Quite a different arrival for her compared to the servicemen and not at all like the one she had imagined during her years in Japan.

⌒

ONCE IN THE CAR, TILLMAN INFORMED IVA SHE WOULD be going to the post office building so she could be arraigned before heading to jail. He added, "Your father is waiting at the arraignment. Quite the homecoming, eh, Iva?"

Iva's heart skipped a beat. Jun would be there. After all this time and what each of them had been through, what would it be like? Iva prayed what her father wrote in his many letters was true and that he would stand by her no matter what. To be face to face with him in handcuffs made her feel ashamed. How could a father not harbor resentment about a daughter who dragged the family name through the mud?

At the federal building, Iva was brought in through the back door. Mercifully there were no reporters present. After going up the elevator and into a long hall, Iva saw her father and June. Breaking free of the agents while still handcuffed, she ran into her father's arms and broke into sobs. "I'm sorry, Daddy. I didn't do anything wrong. How did this get so crazy? Forgive me."

Iva's sister pulled Iva to her and, after a quick hug, said, "You've nothing to apologize for. We know you're innocent, and Dad got the best attorney possible. The lawyer is in the office meeting with the magistrate."

Jun again took his daughter in his arms and said, "It's me that must beg your forgiveness. When you called and said you needed to get out of Japan, I thought you were overreacting. Because I didn't understand, you've had to endure so much. Look at how thin you are. Have they not been feeding you? This situation is my fault."

Tears ran down Iva's face, and her sister wiped them away. Tillman stepped in and took Iva's arm. "Family reunion is over. Come on, let's get this over with."

Once Iva was in the next office, an older, almost-gaunt man with piercing eyes and bushy eyebrows stepped forward to shake her hand. "I'm Wayne Collins, your attorney. From now on, you say nothing and meet with nobody without speaking with me first. Got it?"

"Yes. My husband will be happy to hear someone is helping me read documents."

Collins gave a quizzical look. "This is Magistrate Francis Fox. He's going to read the charges against you, and there are eight. At the end of his reading, you'll enter a plea of not guilty. Ready?"

"Yes."

Collins said, "Before we proceed, Agent Tillman, please remove the handcuffs from my client. Her confinement is unnecessary."

Tillman started to speak, but the magistrate stepped forward and indicated the removal of the restraints. The agent slowly freed Iva.

The elderly magistrate stood and started to read. "In the case between the United States of America and Iva Toguri D'Aquino, you are hereby charged with eight overt acts with treasonable intent and for the purpose of and with the intent to adhere to and give aid and comfort to the Imperial Japanese Government. These acts specifically are as follows: Overt Act I, between March 1, 1944, and May 1, 1944, you worked in the office of the Broadcasting Corporation of Japan and participated in radio broadcasts. Overt Act II, between March 1, 1944, and May 1, 1944, in the offices of the Broadcasting Corporation of Japan, you did discuss with employers the nature and quality of the specific proposed radio broadcasts."

The magistrate droned on as Iva felt more numb to the proceedings. *Of course I discussed broadcasts ahead of time. What did they expect when I was forced to do the announcing? Now he's saying I spoke into a microphone. When one does radio, one speaks into a microphone. Is that possibly a serious charge? Oh God, my head is throbbing, and I don't feel well. Look at my father and sister. What must they be thinking?*

The magistrate continued reading. "Overt Act VI, that on a day during October 1944, the exact date being to the grand jury unknown, in the office of the Broadcasting Corporation of Japan, you did speak into the microphone concerning the loss of ships."

What? Iva scanned her memories. *Did I ever talk about Americans losing ships?*

Two more charges followed. The magistrate turned to Iva and asked, "How do you plead to these eight charges?"

Iva looked at Collins, who nodded to her. "Not guilty. Definitely not guilty."

CHAPTER 27

The next day was Saturday, and Iva was locked in her cell at the county jail. With just one night, she experienced the disadvantages of being in the local jail. The open floorplan ensured that any late-night activity disturbed all the prisoners, and since the night before was Friday, when numerous drunks and prostitutes were arrested, Iva got little sleep.

Collins was visiting to learn more about her experiences for planning the defense. She liked this man not only because of his obvious concern about her but for his past efforts on behalf of Japanese Americans during the war. After yesterday's arraignment, her father explained that while many in the American legal community railed that Japanese American internment was illegal, only Collins stepped forward to fight in court. Although Collins was unsuccessful in winning the case, he did force the Supreme Court to take a stand. One of the first things Collins told Iva in this meeting was that the internment chapter would be a blot on the history of the United States, although it might take many years for people to recognize that.

At 3:30 p.m., there was a knock on the meeting room door. A matron entered and announced that Iva needed to get ready to be picked up by a US marshall.

"Where is she going, and for what reason?" Collins asked.

"I'm not sure. I was called and told to get the prisoner ready for transport."

"The marshall's office closes on weekends, and no one has the right to move my client without an order of the court. Since the courts aren't open today, such an order requires a hearing. Furthermore, no one notified me about this, so this is illegal."

The matron looked at the agitated lawyer who stood between her and Iva. "I'm simply following orders, and she needs to get ready to be picked up."

"Iva, let me check this out. You're not to leave this room until I return." Collins turned to the matron. "I'll hold you personally responsible if my client leaves before I investigate this action. Do you understand?"

The matron looked annoyed and said, "Okay, I'll wait here."

Dashing out, Collins found a telephone and started dialing numbers from his address book. The US marshall's office. No answer. The US attorney's office. Again, no answer. No response at other numbers for the US attorney prosecuting this case or his assistant. Rushing back into the jail, he was relieved to find Iva waiting there with the matron.

"Okay, I'm ready to accompany my client to transportation." Following the matron and Iva, they moved to the rear entrance to the jail where a black sedan waited. Besides the US marshall waiting there, Collins spied an FBI agent in the car. Collins' suspicions that the FBI wanted to conduct an illegal interrogation were confirmed.

"Agent Dunn, what a surprise to see you here. We were just informed the marshall needed to transport Iva, but we were provided no justification. For what purpose are you transporting my client?"

Dunn looked agitated. "None of your business. I was told to pick her up and take her to a meeting. That's all you need to know."

"If you won't inform me what you want my client for, you get me too. Come on, Iva, get in the car."

Iva got in the back seat and was pushed to the other side as Collins climbed in after her. Dunn leaned down and said, "Hey, get out of there, Collins. You're not invited."

"Guess I'm crashing the party."

The marshall and Dunn looked at each other, shrugged as the back door of the car closed, and the group got underway. A short time later, Collins saw that they were stopping behind the local FBI office. As the attorney and his client entered the office, there stood Frederick Tillman.

Without bothering to greet Tillman, Collins launched in. "Why are you attempting to conduct an illegal interrogation of my client? By doing this today, you're deliberately violating the Fourth, Fifth, and Sixth Amendments while also violating legal ethics and courtesy. I demand you cancel this and return my client to her prison."

Tillman looked exasperated. "No one asked you to be here, Wayne. We're taking Iva in the next room, and we have a few questions for her. You cannot accompany her and will be physically restrained if you attempt that."

Collins turned to Iva. "Answer no questions, and state repeatedly that you want your attorney present. Sign nothing."

Iva nodded as she followed Tillman into the next room. In a few minutes, the door opened. Tillman walked out and said to the guards who brought Iva, "Take her back to jail."

Iva emerged smiling.

On the way back to Iva's jail, Collins asked, "What went on in that room?"

"He wanted me to sign a statement that supposedly summarized the interrogation he gave me in Japan. I didn't even look at it and repeatedly demanded that you be present. He gave up quickly."

"Good job. Those guys have no scruples. Repeat that line anytime they try to talk with you alone. When we get back to the jail, let's discuss what we want to present to the judge on Monday about you getting out of jail on bond. If that doesn't work, at least we can try to get you transferred to a facility other than the local jail where the criminals keep you up all night."

"Wayne, why is Agent Tillman so angry and willing to violate the law?"

"There are a lot of people still affected by the war, and he's one of them. It's clear he has it in for you. Rumors are the judge assigned to this case may also be prejudiced against Japanese Americans. It's my job to protect you from people like that who want to hurt you."

Iva settled back, feeling relieved for the first time in many months. *I like this attorney. My dad hired the right guy. Wayne has my best interests at heart and is ready to fight for me, so I need to focus on not letting Tillman get under my skin. If Collins is going to fight, it's time for me to get my energy back and join the struggle, but what did he say about a possible biased judge?*

CHAPTER 28

hile preparing for trial with her defense team, Iva felt more optimistic day by day. They typically met in a small conference room in the courthouse, and Iva was thankful for the chance to get out of her cell. She was escorted every day by Bailiff Herbert Cole, a chubby, middle-aged man who always had a smile for everyone. She became friendly with this kind gentleman and was thankful for his courteous treatment. After a week, Cole got Collins' promise that Iva would not flee, and often the bailiff left the defense team alone for hours on end.

The preparatory meetings were long and exhausting, but Iva found herself growing more energized as the defense strategy developed. The time seemed to fly by, and it was not unusual for Iva to develop cramps after sitting for so long in the old wooden chairs. Though uncomfortable, she laughed to herself. These chairs were still much better than eating and sleeping on the floor in Japan. Her secret highlight each meeting was a lunch break when she invariably ordered a cheeseburger and fries with none of her hated rice.

Collins recruited two attorneys to join the team. Theodore Tamba ("Ted, please, Iva") and George Olshauren would assist. Iva learned that besides charging no fees for their work, the attorneys often paid for expenses out of their own pockets. She liked these men as did her father, who pitched in to cover costs. When Iva asked Jun how he could afford all he was doing, her father stated firmly he had money saved and would borrow whatever else might be needed. "This is the last I want to hear about money, Daughter. You need to focus on winning this case."

The new attorneys told Iva that they joined this case because of their admiration for their lead attorney. Collins had recently won another case he argued in the Supreme Court. During the war, interred Japanese Americans who promised to renounce their US citizenship and leave the country at the end of the war were granted early release. Once the war ended, many wanted to reverse that commitment to leave. By winning in the Supreme Court, over five thousand Japanese Americans would remain in the country with full citizenship. Collins did this all on his own against the might and resources of the government.

Tamba shared that their lead attorney once said, "I've always been drawn to underdogs." He went on to say, "Not only do I admire Wayne's willingness to take on Goliath, but your case is particularly egregious, so I want to be standing with him. The system sometimes thinks it can run over individuals, and that must not be allowed to happen."

Iva hugged Tamba and said, "I cannot tell you how much better I feel now that I have you three lawyers on my side. I was ready to give up."

Already the legal team had scored some small victories. While bail was initially denied, an appeal to the Ninth Circuit Appeals Court reversed that decision. Unfortunately, the court set bail at $50,000, beyond Jun's ability to raise funds. With Iva confined to jail, the defense team won a motion to move her to a facility that provided quieter conditions. In her new cell, Iva was able to get better medical treatment to deal with her chronic dysentery.

While these were positive developments, Iva and the defense team were increasingly worried about the trial judge, Michael "Iron Mike" Roche. At seventy-one, this judge was known for his no-nonsense approach in the courtroom, although he sometimes fell asleep during proceedings. Already Roche showed bias against the defense. Recently he ruled that nineteen witnesses against Iva could travel from Japan at government expense but then surprised Collins by denying any expenses for the defense and refusing to grant immunity to Iva's witnesses. When challenged about this obvious contradiction, Roche refused to explain the decision.

"We're going to have to be careful with this guy," Collins said to the team. "This is a vastly different case from anything he dealt with before, and he appears to have a bias against Japanese Americans. I'm not going to cut him any breaks. When he messes up, I'm going to call him on it. There will be no compromise from our side."

Collins' statement about not giving the judge a break worried Iva. Because she was facing a possible death sentence or more likely a long prison sentence, any compromise that could get her out of this mess sounded better than aggravating the judge.

When reviewing each of the eight charges against her, Collins explained that the government had a difficult time getting the grand jury to bring the charges. The jury agreed to proceed only after Chief Prosecutor

Tom DeWolfe lied by saying Iva was the first of several individuals who would be charged for treason while in Japan. In a subsequent meeting between the prosecutor and Collins, after being repeatedly pressed by the defense counsel as to when additional individuals would be named, DeWolfe said, "There will be no more indictments. Wayne, I'm going to do and say whatever is necessary to win this case. My bosses want a conviction, and I'm the guy who'll deliver that result."

The defense counsel was so angry about this admission of prioritizing a conviction over seeking the truth that he stormed out of the meeting. While debriefing with the defense team, Collins said, "Besides DeWolfe admitting he'll lie if necessary, we also have a judge allowing prosecution witnesses to be flown from Japan to testify. The witnesses who appeared before the grand jury enjoyed an all-expenses-paid vacation in Hawaii before returning to Japan. Meantime, we get no expense money. I don't want us to get discouraged, but the deck is stacked against us."

Tamba added to the team's worries when he reported that Roche again refused money for the defense to fly to Japan to question witnesses. Only after the defense team threatened to appeal this ruling to the Ninth Circuit did Iron Mike grant $3,000 for trip expenses, meaning that Iva's attorneys and Jun would have to cover all additional costs. Tamba told them, "It's hypocritical when the government witnesses are overpaid and we have to scratch and claw for every penny. In previous treason trials the United States prosecuted, including the recently completed one for Axis Sally who collaborated with Germany, compensation for defense witnesses was approved."

Collins said, "It is what it is and another challenge for us. Ted, you need to get ready for your work in Japan. We're counting on you to bring us a full slate of witnesses for Iva." In response to the many requests from the press for a statement about the charges filed against her, Iva issued something simple. "It was a grave disappointment to learn that the grand jury returned an indictment against me. I believe that if the government attorneys were interested, they could have produced before the grand jury any number of material witnesses who would have cleared me of any suspicion of wrongdoing. The army and FBI conducted a complete investigation into my life in Japan and found me innocent. They released me after I was imprisoned for a year. I am innocent of any wrongdoing. I have faith in the court and the jury and believe they will be convinced of my innocence, and I will be acquitted of the charges brought against me."

CHAPTER 29

A month later, Tamba was back from Japan with disappointing results. He couldn't secure one witness willing to come to the United States and testify on Iva's behalf. Many individuals he spoke with said off the record that the FBI visited them before Tamba's arrival and threatened them with harsh consequences if they cooperated with Iva's defense. Some were told their hope to gain or regain US citizenship would be thwarted if they cooperated. Others were threatened that occupation authorities would take away their jobs and jail them.

"I've never seen such scared people in my life," Tamba explained. "The FBI visited all forty-three of the potential witnesses before I arrived, and I consider it a miracle I was able to get nineteen of them to give me a deposition supporting Iva. Even your friend Ruth Hayakawa confidentially observed several of the prosecution witnesses testifying are only doing it to get expense money from the United States. Ruth went on to explain that several witnesses knew they were committing perjury, but the threats of the FBI and lure of money were too much to resist."

This news crushed Iva. *I knew many at Radio Tokyo disliked me because I was openly supportive of the Allied war effort, but could that possibly justify perjury? Ruth exposed what is going on, so at least my defense team knows what we're up against.*

Collins said, "Depositions never work as well with a jury as actual witnesses, but at least we have something. Good work, Ted. Now let's focus on the key witnesses we will have. First is Charles Cousens, who is committed to being here. He wrote to me that he once promised to protect you and won't let you down now. The fact that he was tried in Australia for treason and exonerated should play well here. It's telling that six months ago he went to the American embassy in Australia and said he wanted to testify on your behalf. Only recently did the embassy pass that information on. He's also bringing another POW from Bunka, Kenneth Parkyns, whose life you saved because of medicine smuggled into their prison camp. Did you know Parkyns well?"

"No. I remember hearing his name from Cousens, but I never met him," Iva said.

"He's committed to trying to pay back what you did. Next is Ted Ince. He's also one hundred percent in our corner. Since he was right there at the radio station with you, that should be positive. The troublesome one is Norman Reyes. He's filed an affidavit saying you were treasonous, which I suspect is because the FBI is threatening to take away his current student visa to study in Nashville. Is there any other possible reason why he turned against you?"

"Nothing I can think of. Norman's testimony is disappointing, but he was treated differently by the Japanese once he wasn't a POW anymore. Major Cousens used to say Norman was more concerned with his career and would do anything if the Japanese pressured him. Since the FBI is now leaning on him, I'm not surprised."

Collins said, "That's also what your major said to me. Cousens promised he'd do all he could once he got here to turn Reyes around. We'll have to pray for his Australian charm to work."

AT THE SAN FRANCISCO AIRPORT, TAMBA WAS SURPRISED when the plane emptied and neither Cousens nor Parkyns appeared. Suspecting foul play, Tamba called Collins, who started working his contacts. Soon the lead attorney appeared at the airport, saying, "Let's get down to the customs area. I was told off the record Tillman has them sequestered there."

After opening doors to various rooms and apologizing repeatedly, the attorneys struck gold. Led by Tillman, several FBI agents were grilling the Australians.

"Well, look what we have here," Collins said as he pushed past the agents attempting to block his way. "Another illegal and unethical move, Agent Tillman. The court will love to hear about this. Should I call the judge now, or do these tired travelers leave with me?"

Tillman's anger was apparent, but he sputtered, "Go ahead and take these two. It's not going to make a difference in the end."

WHEN THE AUSTRALIANS WALKED INTO THE DEFENSE team's meeting room the next day, Iva jumped up and rushed into Cousens' arms. "Thank you for coming. I knew I could count on you. You were the one person who gave me a reason to keep going for so long in Japan, and now you're here to help me again." Separating from Cousens as she wiped tears from her eyes, Iva turned to Parkyns. Hugging him, she said, "I know I never met you, so thanks for making this trip."

"Thank you, Iva," Parkyns said. "You saved my life with that medicine that you got for us. It's the least I could do."

Introductions with the team followed, including Jun bowing before Cousens and thanking him for taking such good care of his daughter.

"It's our pleasure, Mr. Toguri," Cousens said, "although I have to say your country doesn't put out much of a welcome mat for a couple of blokes like ourselves."

Cousens and Parkyns explained how the FBI agents threatened deportation unless they agreed to change their testimony and come over to the prosecution side. Cousens laughed as he said, "Seeing Mr. Collins come charging through that door was like the cavalry arriving in one of your Westerns. Most timely."

Collins chuckled. "That was fun, eh, Ted? Best now for us to get to work. Any luck contacting Norman Reyes last night, Charles?"

Cousens nodded. "I did get a hold of Norman. An FBI threat to revoke his student visa is why he agreed to work with them. After a short talk about how we need to do right by Iva, he agreed to change his testimony."

"Good work and so fast. Ted, you get in touch with Reyes, and make sure the FBI doesn't get him turned around again. Now let's start working on your testimony."

Smiling and holding Cousens' hand, Iva asked, "When does Filipe, my other star witness, get here?"

Collins said, "Filipe is scheduled to arrive tomorrow. With what happened yesterday, we'd better have a couple of us at the docks when his ship arrives."

THERE WAS A REPEAT OF THE AUSTRALIANS' EXPERIENCE, but this time, the defense team was unable to find Filipe despite appeals to the court. Days later, the FBI released Iva's husband and allowed him to contact the defense team.

Collins learned that for two days, the FBI threatened Filipe that he would be charged and put on trial for assisting Iva in treasonous acts against the United States. Iva's husband kept asking how, as a non-American, he could be tried for treason. When the FBI realized its threats weren't going to get him on the next ship back to Japan, it forced him to sign a document strictly limiting his visa for the term of his wife's trial. At that time, he would leave the United States and never be allowed to return for the rest of his life. Collins was impressed at the lengths the FBI was going to intimidate witnesses.

When he reached the jail, Collins led Filipe to Iva's cell. Iva rushed to the bars and embraced him as best she could.

"Because it's so late in the day," Collins said, "the jail authorities won't allow you out of your cell, and Filipe can visit for only thirty minutes. Tomorrow we'll get the two of you in a room so that you can visit quietly. I'll wait out in the corridor until we must leave. I'm sorry it has to be this way."

Iva barely heard her attorney as she held Filipe's arms, but as she looked into her husband's eyes, Iva knew things had changed between them.

CHAPTER 30

It was the evening before the start of her trial, and Iva was having one last piece of birthday cake. Because of Collins' appeals for visitation privileges, Jun was coming daily and bringing Iva fruit and other foods to help fight the lingering impacts of dysentery. The cake and celebration with her father and defense team, between last-minute preparations for court, had been a nice break. It also highlighted how different her current circumstances were. Her typical day in jail was waiting tables, acting as an informal nurse for the other female prisoners, and reading. Her nickname in jail was "Little Nurse." Those activities helped her keep her sanity and pass the hours of boredom. With the trial starting, Iva allowed herself to hope that this would lead to gaining her freedom.

Everyone she came in contact with asked how she felt on the eve of the trial. She told them she was confident that all would go well since the truth must win out, although, to herself, she worried. The truth had not been a sure bet in the past. Collins often stated, "Given how general and vague the charges are, and with the defense discovery about FBI misconduct with witnesses, we're likely to win. Remember, all trials have twists and turns, and much will ride on the quality of your testimony."

She often thought about Collins' words, and her growing nervousness was aggravating her dysentery. *I want to get this over and to go back to living quietly with my family. Maybe then my health will get back to normal.*

Another challenge for the defense was the prosecution's request, the month before, for another delay, adding more cost for Iva's father, who was now deep in debt. The judge granted that delay, and the defense concluded that it was to allow the FBI, led by Tillman, to harass and threaten the defense witnesses one last time. Fortunately the individuals testifying for Iva ignored the last-minute FBI intimidation.

When alone that night, Iva thought about her situation with Filipe. Her sense that things had changed was proving true. Although he visited daily, there was a distance between them concerning their future. Remembering the day when things came to a head, Iva squeezed her eyes shut to avoid crying.

"Iva, tell me how this is going to work." Filipe was angry. "You said that if you're acquitted, you're going to remain in the United States as you've always wanted. How can we be married when the government has forced me to sign a document that says I only have a temporary visa for the trial and once I leave America I can never return?"

"Why did you sign that?"

He threw his hands up in frustration. "They had me locked up for two days and said unless I agreed, they'd send me back to Japan. I thought it was important to be here to testify on your behalf. What else could I do? Your attorney agrees it was wrong of them to do that, but he also said I had no choice."

"I don't want to get divorced."

"Neither do I. We're Catholic, and the Church doesn't recognize divorce. No matter how this all plays out, we're married for life."

Iva turned away to hide her frustration. This man was her husband and the father of their stillborn baby. He was the one who had stood by her during the awful days in Japan along with his wonderful mother. Now she looked up at him with sadness.

Filipe's irritation boiled over as he pointed at Iva and said, "After the trial, either you move to Japan to be with me or we move together to Portugal. You can make periodic trips to visit your family, although I won't be able to accompany you. That's the only way we can be together."

Iva said nothing as she stared at her husband. *I've only wanted to live in America with my family. That's been my goal from the first day of the war, and nothing has changed in my thinking. Why does it have to be like this?*

When his wife said nothing, Filipe grabbed his hat. "Iva, I love you, but it looks like what you said while in prison back in Japan has come true. The US government is out to destroy our marriage, and you're helping them."

CHAPTER 31

Walking into the courtroom accompanied by Bailiff Cole, Iva was not surprised to see every seat taken. Collins told her later that if any seats were left open at the lunch break, there was a line outside waiting to fill them.

Jun, her sister June, June's husband, and Filipe sat in the front row. Fred and Inez wanted to be there but couldn't get off work. Her family waved, which helped a bit with Iva's nervousness. She noticed that not one other Japanese American was present. Collins often railed against the Japanese American Citizens League for not taking a public stance to support her. Tamba explained that the group's silence was primarily out of fear, given the raw feelings and racism that had carried over from the war. One day he said, "They'll come to recognize the crime, but given the current political environment, they're choosing to stay silent."

The jury filed in—six white men and six white women. The jury selection process had been contentious among the defense team. It had taken only two hours to choose this jury.

Afterward, Tamba complained to Collins that he hadn't objected to the actions of the prosecution more forcefully. "Wayne, you let them preemptively challenge every minority who was in the group. That kicked out six Negros and one Chinese. The prosecution was so bold they made the minority jury candidates wait in a separate room from the whites, and you didn't point that out to the judge. The prosecution team paid attention to previous treason trials and how minorities tended to favor the defense. We just lost an important opportunity."

"Calm down, Ted. We'll be fine. We have six women on the jury, and I'm sure they'll be sympathetic to Iva. If somehow we lose, the all-white jury is an argument we can use in appeals."

Tamba walked away, shaking his head. This confrontation made Iva nervous, but given all that Collins was sacrificing for her, she prayed he was right.

Slowly taking her seat at the defense table, Iva could feel all twelve jurors staring at her. She felt self-conscious, since she was wearing the same green plaid two-piece suit that had been her work outfit during the years in Japan. Collins insisted on this strategy since he didn't want her to look well-to-do or exotic but like a woman without means.

Iva pushed back on this strategy. "Let me get this straight, Wayne. For what's supposed to be a long trial, you want me to wear the same clothes? They'll be completely worn out by the end."

"Good. The more worn the better. You can wash your suit on weekends, but I want to see you only in that god-awful outfit. Try to look small and nonthreatening."

At the prosecution table, Iva saw DeWolfe, the lead attorney. Sitting close by was the Senior US Attorney Frank Hennessey. Collins explained that normally Hennessey would be the lead, but rumor had it that he'd informed his bosses this was a weak case. The superiors at Justice then picked DeWolfe to conduct the case. There was another rumor that DeWolfe had written a memo expressing reservations about proceeding with this case, but when the defense tried to secure a copy, Justice said all DeWolfe's documents were now classified top secret.

The door to the judge's chambers opened, and Roche entered looking like a frail seventy-one-year-old man. Iva thought she saw Roche look her way and sneer as he ordered everyone to sit. Was it possible the judge had done that, or was it her imagination?

"Ladies and gentlemen of the jury, I have only one more point to make to you that is critical to this case."

DeWolfe's opening argument had been going on for almost forty minutes. As Iva listened, she thought much of what the prosecutor said was absolute fiction. More than once she wanted to jump up and say, "That's not true. I didn't do any of what he described." She prayed for the truth to be enough, but it was apparent her story would be stacked up against this pack of lies.

The prosecutor went on. "My final point is to dismiss any question about the citizenship of Mrs. D'Aquino. It's true she married a Portuguese citizen in Japan and was eligible to become a citizen of that country but chose not to. At no time did she renounce her American citizenship, and instead, she acted against her country while claiming to be loyal."

Collins turned and looked at Iva. Portuguese citizenship was to be an argument if later in the trial Collins thought things weren't going well. Now that strategy was no longer viable.

DeWolfe stood close to the jury as he concluded. "This is one of the most despicable cases of treason against our country at a time of national emergency. I will show you why Mrs. D'Aquino deserves to be found guilty and given significant punishment for her crimes."

Judge Roche leaned forward. "The prosecution may call its first witness."

The defense wouldn't present their opening arguments until they presented their witnesses. Now it was all prosecution.

AFTER FINISHING WITH HIS FIRST WITNESS, DEWOLFE said, "No further questions, Your Honor."

Collins stood and approached the guard who worked at Sugamo Prison when Iva was held there. The only point the witness had made was that he had a ¥1 note Iva signed as "Tokyo Rose." Collins said, "Did my client ever refer to herself as Tokyo Rose in any of the conversations you had with her?"

"No."

"Might my client have signed as Tokyo Rose to make you and others who were hounding her for an autograph go away?"

"I don't know. There were a lot of people asking her to sign things as Tokyo Rose."

"Are you aware that several female radio announcers worked during the war at Radio Tokyo?"

"Yes."

"Might anyone of them have also been known as Tokyo Rose?"

"I suppose."

"No further questions, Your Honor."

⌒

AFTER A BRIEF BREAK, THE FIRST KEY WITNESS TOOK the stand: Colonel Shigatsuga Tsuneishi, the army commander at Radio Tokyo. He sat ramrod straight in the witness box.

Colonel. He must have been promoted at the end of the war even though the propaganda efforts he led at the radio station proved worthless.

Tsuneishi's testimony about his duties managing army programs at the radio station and making sure maximum benefit was gained through propaganda was succinct. He took credit for developing the *Zero Hour* program and stated no one who worked at the radio station, including POWs and Iva, were ever threatened to gain their participation. Iva was not only a willing participant, but she volunteered to write scripts that attacked the US military.

Iva seethed and bit her lip as she listened to this fabrication. She never once wrote a script. Her job was strictly to read introductions for the music. Tamba put his hand on Iva's arm to calm her down as Collins stepped forward.

After revisiting the colonel's role and duties, the defense attorney asked, "When you first approached Major Cousens about working for the radio station, did he refuse to help you?"

"At first he said he didn't want to work there," Tsuneishi said.

"Isn't it the case that as you discussed why Major Cousens was needed, you unsheathed your battle sword and placed it on the table in front of you?

"Yes."

"Since Japanese battle swords are often used to behead prisoners or criminals, do you think that was a clear threat to Major Cousens?"

"I only encouraged the major. I never threatened him."

"Pretty strong encouragement. By the way, wasn't there another POW who refused to participate? I believe his last name was Williams."

"I don't know what happened to him."

"Really? Mr. Williams was a prisoner who refused to work at Radio Tokyo. Is that correct?"

Tsuneishi bristled as he replied. "Yes."

"What happened to prisoner Williams?"

Breathing deeply, the Japanese colonel again said, "I don't know."

"I do, Colonel Tsuneishi. He disappeared one night."

The witness was silent and looking straight ahead.

Collins continued. "Don't you think, Colonel, that other prisoners such as Major Cousens would notice when someone refuses one of your offers and then disappears? You dare to sit here and say you never coerced prisoners."

Tsuneishi continued staring at the defense attorney.

Collins stared back. "Oh, one last question, Colonel. Please tell me the specific scripts Mrs. D'Aquino wrote for the *Zero Hour*."

"I cannot remember them specifically."

"You cannot remember because she never wrote a single script. Her job was only to introduce musical recordings during the entertainment portion of the broadcasts. There were others whose job it was to write scripts that announcers read. Isn't that true?"

After a pause, Tsuneishi said, "Yes."

Collins started to return to the defense counsel's table when he turned back. "I guess I have still another question. How many women announcers worked on *Zero Hour* broadcasts at Radio Tokyo?"

"I am not sure."

"More than one?"

"Yes."

"My research showed there were twelve different female announcers who were at one time or another on the *Zero Hour*. Do you dispute that?"

"No."

"No further questions, Your Honor."

FOLLOWING DEWOLFE'S QUESTIONING OF CLARK LEE regarding the specifics of his and Brundidge's initial interview with Iva, Collins started his cross-examination. "Mr. Lee, are you the author of the book *One Last Look Around* published in 1947 where you write about your years covering the war in the Pacific?"

Lee shifted in discomfort in his chair and licked his lips as the reporter now realized Collins was going to use this book against him. "Yeah, I wrote that," Lee said.

"Is there not a chapter entitled 'The Noose Around Her Neck' in which you describe your commitment to finding and bringing Iva Toguri to justice?"

"Yeah."

"Good. Let's start to go through that chapter and what you wrote there and compare that with some of the specifics presented by the prosecution."

Lee closed his eyes as Collins started to list the obvious exaggerations and outright mistruths Lee concocted in his book and how they contradicted his testimony during depositions and grand jury testimony.

Lee's perspiration thoroughly soaked his shirt. Despite repeated objections from DeWolfe, most of them upheld by Judge Roche, it was apparent that Lee's credibility was shattered. It was getting late in the day, but Collins had one more blow to land.

"Mr. Lee, turning away from your book now, isn't it true you contacted me and requested a meeting at the St. Francis Hotel on October 25 of last year?"

Lee's eyes grew wide as he realized where the defense counsel was going. Lowering his head, the witness almost whispered, "Yeah."

"Who is Hirumo Yagi?"

Taking in a deep breath, Lee said, "Yagi worked for a travel agency in Tokyo."

"At our meeting, didn't you say you wanted me to be aware that your partner in that original interview, Harry Brundidge, bribed Mr. Yagi to testify before the grand jury? Mr. Yagi was instructed to say that my client made treasonous broadcasts even though he never visited Radio Tokyo or heard any such broadcasts. I believe the FBI gave Yagi a new suit of clothes and a free vacation in the United States for his testimony. Is that correct?"

"Objection, Your Honor," DeWolfe cried as he jumped to his feet. "This is not true. All witnesses have sworn an oath."

"It's true," Collins said. "We'll prove it when Mr. Brundidge testifies tomorrow."

Roche looked at the two attorneys who were staring at each other. He said, "The jury will ignore this last exchange between the attorneys. Mr. Collins, you appear to have made your point. It's late in the day. Do you have any more questions for this witness?"

Looking at the judge and weighing his options of trying to go after Lee one more time, Collins thought back to his co-counsel's advice to not aggravate the judge. "No further questions, Your Honor."

THE NEXT MORNING, THE DEFENSE TEAM WAS CELEBRATING the previous day and anticipating Brundidge's testimony. Collins broke into laughter and said, "I can't wait to get at that second-rate hack journalist with his documented history of making things up. Iva was only a way for Brundidge to promote himself. We got 'em. We got 'em!"

Tamba reminded Collins that DeWolfe's strategy of constant objections and Roche's tendency to sustain them was a bad sign. Still, Iva's optimism had never been higher.

With Lee's admission about the prosecution's bribery to secure a perjured witness, the judge should have dismissed all charges and declared the trial over. Since Judge Roche was not taking any action against the prosecution based upon Lee's testimony, Collins said that today would put Roche on the spot when he questioned Brundidge.

There was a knock on the meeting room door, and a court official entered. "Note here from the judge."

Collins took the note and read it aloud. "The prosecution has dropped Mr. Brundidge as a witness, since he suddenly took ill and had to leave San Francisco last night. Agent Tillman will be the next witness."

The room was silent. "Those bastards," Collins said as he pounded his fist on the table. "Wait until I get into court and start after Roche for allowing this."

Tamba said, "Good luck on that one, Wayne. In the meantime, we have only a short time to prep for Tillman."

The attorneys started to pull out their notes for the FBI agent and figure out what they needed to change based upon the events of the day before.

Iva looked down at the floor. *Is there anything the government won't do to get me?*

"AGENT TILLMAN, I HAVE ONLY A FEW QUESTIONS," Collins said. "On July 27, did you meet with a member of the defense team, Theodore Tamba?"

Tillman exhaled loudly and stared at the defense counsel. "I did."

"At that time, did you tell Mr. Tamba that Mr. Yagi confessed to you he had been bribed to lie to the grand jury?"

DeWolfe said tiredly, "Objection, Your Honor." Collins looked at his opponent and had the clear impression DeWolfe was going through the motions since he knew this was all true.

Roche gave DeWolfe a long look. "Objection overruled. The witness will answer the question."

Tillman said, "Yes."

Collins rubbed his hands together, and a small smile escaped him. "Let's get into the specifics of that bribery."

De Wolfe stood again. "Objection, Your Honor. The witness has admitted to the point, and there's no need for further elaboration at this time. We're here trying the accused for her treasonous acts, not trying the FBI."

Roche said, "Objection sustained. Mr. Collins, there shall be no further follow up on this topic. Your point is noted."

"But Your Honor, it's important to clarify..."

Judge Roche banged his gavel. "Did you hear me, Mr. Collins? Move on with your questioning."

The defense counsel stared at the judge, turned, and looked at his team. Iva caught his eye, and Collins could see how much she wanted him to grill the FBI agent further. Turning back to the judge, Collins quietly said, "No additional questions."

As Collins and the defense team left the courtroom that afternoon, a prosecution witness who was soon to testify approached. Seizo Hyuga stood close and said, "Mr. Collins, may we speak quietly?"

They ducked into an empty conference room. Hyuga said to Iva's lead counsel, "As you know, I was the liaison between Colonel Tsuneishi and the radio management. I now realize what a mistake it was to agree to testify against Iva. The FBI put tremendous pressure on me and made threats to my family if I did not cooperate, but I cannot go through with perjury. If you ask me tomorrow about threats the colonel made to Iva and others, I can confirm he lied. I will also state that since I had to monitor all broadcasts, your client never made any treasonous statements. She was always a major problem, resisting all of the pressure the colonel put on her."

Smiling, Collins shook Hyuga's hand. "Thank you for your willingness to tell the truth. I'll make sure to cover those points in my questioning, and I know Iva would want me to thank you."

"No need for thanks. I'm sorry it has taken me so long to see the right thing that must be done."

The two men opened the conference room door, and there stood DeWolfe and another member of his team. Looking directly at Hyuga, DeWolfe's eyes narrowed.

THE NEXT MORNING WAS A REPEAT OF WHAT HAD HAP-pened with Brundidge. When Tamba went looking for Seizo Hyuga, a reporter said DeWolfe had told him at coffee that a family member was seriously ill back in Japan, and Hyuga was on his way home. Tamba went looking for Collins to report this news. The lawyers cursed the prosecution again, and Tamba said, "Better luck today getting any relief from Roche on this. He ignored your protests about Brundidge disappearing, and he'll probably do the same today. DeWolfe will argue Hyuga was a minor witness, and his deposition is in the record even though we know it doesn't represent what he wanted to recant. Face it. They snookered us again."

THE MOST IMPORTANT WITNESSES FOR THE PROSECUTION were up next: Kenkichi Oki and George Mitsushio, Iva's supervisors at Radio Tokyo. Like with previous witnesses,

DeWolfe seemed anxious to get their testimony on the record quickly and then turn them over to the defense. Oki took the stand first, followed by Mitsushio. Iva clenched her fists during their testimonies and continually fought her desire to stand and call them liars. She prayed the jury could see that they were perjuring themselves.

Collins went right to the heart of Oki's weak testimony. "You stated in your testimony specific language my client used for several days in October 1944 that demonstrated her treason. You have an incredible memory, Mr. Oki."

Oki licked his lips. "Thank you. It is good."

"What did other female announcers specifically say during their broadcasts on each of those days? Let's start with Ruth Hayakawa."

Fidgeting in his seat and looking toward the prosecution's table, Oki said, "I don't know."

"Not such a good memory there. How about June Suyama? What did she specifically say on those days?"

"I don't know."

"How about what you had for breakfast on October 20, 1944?"

Oki looked baffled and embarrassed. "I can't remember."

"Hmm. As someone born in the United States, educated here, and living in Japan for only a few years, I'm sure with your strong memory you're able to repeat the Pledge of Allegiance. Could you please recite that for me now?"

Oki drew in a breath. "I pledge allegiance to the flag of the United States of America and…"

The entire courtroom stared as the witness was quiet. That long silence was interrupted when Judge Roche stepped in and completed the rest of the pledge.

"Thank you, Your Honor." Returning to the defense table, Collins winked at his team while picking up two packets of paper. He turned and faced the witness. "I have here a copy of your deposition and that of George Mitsushio. Do you remember swearing an oath to tell the truth in that deposition?"

Oki was clearly uncomfortable. "Yes."

"What's amazing to me is that when I read many sections of your depositions, they are the same, word for word, page after page. These exact words were used by you today in answering Mr. DeWolfe. It's almost like you were coached to memorize specific statements. Were you coached by the FBI before the trial as to your specific testimony in the deposition and here today?"

Oki no longer looked at the prosecution table but up toward the ceiling. "Yes."

With Mitsushio, Collins was able to get more details about the morning coaching sessions where Tillman and others drilled the former managers on the specific words they would say. After Mitsushio's testimony, the court was adjourned for the day.

June leaned over the rail separating them and said to Iva, "After the testimony of your supervisors, the press is laying odds ten to one that you'll be acquitted. Sleep well tonight, my sister."

Iva almost floated next to Bailiff Cole as she returned to her cell.

THE FINAL WITNESSES FOR THE PROSECUTION WERE servicemen who had responded to the FBI's national request for anyone who heard Iva's broadcasts and could cite trea-sonous statements. Collins made quick work of the testi-monies by asking how someone listening to a long-distance broadcast could tell one female announcer from another. He questioned how each witness could remember specific broadcasts and wording when those individuals could not remember other specifics on those days. After this parade of witnesses, the prosecution rested.

That night, Iva tossed and turned. *Finally my side of the story will be told. Despite the prosecution's tricks, Wayne thinks we're in good shape. I know Cousens will do well on the stand, but I worry about Reyes. My testimony will be critical, and the prosecutor and judge truly scare me. I wish I didn't have to get up there and could go home right now.*

CHAPTER 32

Tamba gave the opening argument for the defense. Collins agreed that Judge Roche might be getting worn down by the lead counsel's badgering, and this type of presentation was the co-counsel's strength. The defense planned to weave information into the opening argument that normally wouldn't be allowed during questioning, so it was another benefit to let Tamba spar with the prosecution and judge on those marginal issues.

Painting a detailed picture of the constant harassment Iva was under by the secret police during the war years in Japan, Tamba described how she continually refused to become a Japanese citizen. The price she paid was not to get a ration card for needed food. Tamba went into detail about how Iva had to get a job to survive and once at Radio Tokyo was forced into broadcasting.

Tamba addressed the critical issue of the crime Iva was charged with. "To prove the charge of treason, a person not only has to have the ability to betray their country but must also have the committed intent to do so. Does this endless harassment by Japanese authorities sound like it would be needed if our client was a willing participant? Does Iva Toguri sound like she planned to commit treason if she risked her freedom to smuggle food and medicine to American POWs? Clearly not. You'll soon learn how our client worked to sabotage enemy broadcasts at great risk to herself."

Tamba launched into the issue of the prosecution witnesses being coerced and bribed by the FBI, starting with Harry Brundidge.

"Objection, Your Honor," DeWolfe said. "This is hearsay and not relevant to the treason of the accused."

"Your honor," Tamba replied, "I can prove the specifics of several briberies and that tampering is relevant to prove the innocence of our client."

Judge Roche stared down at the defense counsel. After a long minute, he said, "You'd better be able to prove that, Mr. Tamba. I am reluctantly overruling the objection. Please proceed."

Tamba caught his breath. Collins had been right in thinking they should take this risk even though the defense team didn't possess the specific details of the bribery. Most importantly, the jury was again hearing about prosecution coercion.

THE FIRST WITNESS FOR THE DEFENSE WAS CHARLES Cousens. Collins was back taking the lead, and he spent his initial questioning to chronicle the adverse conditions the Australian and other POWs experienced. Cousens struggled to control his emotions while describing prisoners being tortured or beaten to death. The prosecution objected, saying the stories weren't relevant to possible threats made to Iva. Collins explained that Major Cousens shared many of his experiences with Iva, so she was well aware of the extremes the Japanese would go to if one didn't cooperate. Roche said, "Objection overruled."

As he approached the bench, DeWolfe said, "Your Honor, I must object. I believe your ruling is against legal precedent. I request an immediate recess so I can do some research."

The judge looked annoyed. "We'll take a thirty-minute recess."

After the break, as the defense team reentered the courtroom, Collins spied DeWolfe exiting the judge's chambers. The smiling prosecutor gave his adversary a wink as he walked back to his table. A moment later, the judge entered.

Roche spoke. "After reviewing my law books, I'm convinced I ruled inappropriately about the admissibility of testimony from others regarding how they might have been threatened during the war. The focus here is on the experiences of the accused. The jury will strike the testimony on Major Cousens' experiences in their deliberations. Mr. Collins, you may proceed, and I warn you for the remainder of this witness's testimony and that of subsequent witnesses to avoid this line of questioning."

Collins stood there stunned. What had gone on in that chamber without him present? DeWolfe had outmaneuvered him again.

⌐——⌐

WHEN THE TESTIMONY OF THE AUSTRALIAN POW WAS completed, it was on the record that Iva never wrote her scripts, and her job was only to introduce records. The effort to sabotage the broadcasts through satire was made clear, as well as that it frustrated Radio Tokyo station management that Iva was never cooperative in doing anything that might be construed as propaganda.

The prosecution rose for cross-examination. Cousens' character was attacked, and he was accused of being a Japanese collaborator and coaching Iva to betray her country. To reinforce that the Australian supported the Japanese, DeWolfe produced receipts from dinners Cousens attended as part of his work at Radio Tokyo. "Hard to believe you were suffering, Major, when I see how many dinners you attended where you even ate ice cream."

Cousens bristled. "I was required to attend those dinners. When I ate dinner out, I made sure my rations back at the prison camp went to another. By the end of the war, I weighed 140 pounds."

"You did better than most, Major. I see you also were tried for treason once you got home to Australia."

"I was fully exonerated."

"Maybe your countrymen aren't as thorough as we are here. No further questions."

NEXT UP FOR THE DEFENSE WAS TED INCE, WHO WAS still in the army and recently promoted to major. Before the trial, the Justice Department threatened Ince that if he testified for Iva, the government would pursue a charge of treason against him. As a result, Ince declined to testify. Collins convinced him that should the United States bring treason charges against him, Ince's attorney would want Iva as a witness. Collins stood before the reluctant witness.

Ince sat in the witness box impressively bolt upright in full uniform. He repeatedly confirmed Iva never said anything treasonous and that Cousens intended to sabotage the broadcasts. Over the objections of the prosecution, Ince affirmed that she smuggled goods into Bunka and saved prisoners' lives. In closing, the major affirmed that Iva brought war news she had learned through her husband to the POWs, and that kept spirits up, further indicating her support for the Allies.

DeWolfe went lightly in his cross. When he asked Ince if he trusted Iva, Ince said, "No, and I told Cousens to be careful with her. No Japanese can be trusted."

"Objection, Your Honor," said Collins. "My client is a citizen of the United States and isn't Japanese."

"Objection overruled," Roche said.

The exasperated Collins sat down, trying to control his emotions. Later, in requestioning Ince, the defense counsel asked whether, even though Ince never trusted Iva because of her Japanese ancestry, he could cite any instance where she committed an act of treason.

"No," Ted Ince said, "although I must clarify that the Japanese removed me from Radio Tokyo before the time your client allegedly said American ships were lost and servicemen would have no way to get home."

Collins was surprised Ince made this point on his own and decided not to ask Ince anything more about his statement, concluding that the specific broadcast would be discussed in detail later in the trial.

Next up was Norman Reyes. Collins knew from the start Reyes would prove a difficult witness, but since the Filipino was part of the broadcast team, there was no choice. Reyes' revised testimony contradicted his original deposition given under duress. The defense counsel knew whenever a witness gave conflicting statements, their credibility was tenuous at best. The best strategy was to limit initial questioning and try to correct prosecutorial damage when Collins revisited the witness.

In questioning by Collins, Reyes proved to be a good witness. He affirmed Iva's efforts to resist the Japanese and assist the POWs at great risk. The Filipino provided examples of how the *Zero Hour* team worked to sabotage the broadcasts in many small ways. To the defense team's surprise, Reyes said he had heard Colonel Tsuneishi refer at least once to Iva as Tokyo Rose.

Collins focused on this unexpected statement. Reyes stuck to his guns, saying that he specifically recalled the reference but conceded there were never any other cases where this title was assigned to Iva. He conceded any of the other female announcers might have been called Tokyo Rose by others.

In closing, Collins asked if Reyes trusted Iva in their work. The Filipino said, "I would have trusted her with my life."

DeWolfe moved forward and stood close to Reyes. Within a few minutes, through rapid-fire questioning, the prosecutor had the intimidated witness struggling to answer questions regarding loyalty based upon his mixed-race ancestry.

Collins stood. "Objection, Your Honor. Counsel is badgering the witness, and what's the purpose of discussing his ancestry other than to play the race card?"

"Objection overruled. Sit down, Mr. Collins."

DeWolfe again lit into Reyes, who struggled to remember specific dates and instances. Getting to the issue of how his current testimony contradicted his previous statements to the FBI, DeWolfe said, "Do you tell the truth, Norman?"

"Yes, sir, I do."

"Do you tell the truth all the time?"

"Yes."

"So you told the truth to the FBI when they interviewed you, correct?"

"Yes, but they wrote it down differently than what I said. Agent Tillman said I'd have the opportunity to correct it later."

"But you told them the truth, right, Norman?

"Yes, but…"

"No further questions, Your Honor, for this witness who likes to tell different stories to different people."

Collins had his work cut out for him. After getting Reyes calmed down and giving him the chance to think between questions, Collins made the point that the FBI never gave Reyes a chance to correct his interview. The defense attorney next got on the record that the FBI had threatened to have Reyes' student visa canceled if he didn't cooperate. Returning to the prosecution's questions about his racial background, Collins asked, "Isn't it a fact your wife was living in the Philippines under Japanese rule while you were in Japan?"

DeWolfe called, "Objection, Your Honor. It's not relevant where the witness's wife was living."

Collins bit his lip. "Your Honor, the prosecution opened this subject of Mr. Reyes' racial background, and the fact that his wife lived under Japanese control is relevant."

"Objection sustained."

"But Your Honor…"

"I said sustained, Mr. Collins. Finish your questions or sit down."

<hr />

IVA WAS DEPRESSED WHEN SHE MET WITH THE DEFENSE team that evening. Her optimism had been crushed by Judge Roche making one arbitrary ruling after another against the defense. "Why does the judge seem to hate me so?" she asked.

Collins shook his head. Tamba said, "I'll be candid. I think he's just like Ince. He hates anyone Japanese. At least Ince owns his hatred. Roche seems to be carrying his extreme feelings from the days of the war into today."

"All the more reason your testimony will be critical, Iva," Collins said. "In the meantime, let's get ready for tomorrow. We have a fair number of witnesses and need to put those depositions Ted got on the record."

Iva started to cry. "I don't know how good a witness I can be when the judge is out for me. What chance do I have?"

Collins came around the table and put his hand on his client's shoulder. "I know it's not looking good right now, but I'm sure we're going to win. Why don't you take a break and get some rest since we've got a long night ahead of us. That make sense?"

Iva looked up through her tears. "Okay. You still think we're going to win?"

"Sure. Now go get some rest."

After Iva left, Collins sat down and looked at his team. Tamba said, "Do you really think we're going to win, Wayne?"

Collins looked down. "I don't know, but we need to get to work if we're going to stand any chance."

Later in her cell, Iva was surprised by a visitor. "Dad, what're you doing here? Evenings are not the time you usually visit."

Jun said, "Wayne called saying you were feeling down, so I thought I should check on you. You need your rest, but do you mind an old Japanese man sharing some thoughts?"

"Not at all. It's good to see you, and Wayne's right. I'm getting worn down by this judge, since almost every ruling is against us. I was hopeful at the start of the trial that the truth would win out, but the prosecution twists everything, ships out witnesses who might help our side, and relies on the judge to limit what our team is trying to do."

"This guy is bad, Iva. Sometimes I stare at him, and never once will he look at us. This man hates the Japanese. I know Collins is doing the best he can."

"I can't complain about Wayne, although I know Ted and George think he's making some mistakes. I don't want to go to prison, Dad. I know now I should have listened more to people like Filipe years ago, but I was too focused on getting back to our family. When I get past this, I'm going to do more listening and think of others more." Iva lowered her head into her hands and started to cry. Her whole body was shaking.

Reaching through the bars, Jun tried to pull his daughter as close as possible. "It's not over yet, Daughter. Tomorrow Filipe testifies, and I'm sure he'll be a good witness. How are the two of you doing? I noticed he's not visiting you every day, although he's in the courtroom."

Through a new round of tears, she said, "Oh, Dad, that's not good either. I don't know what's going to happen to my marriage."

Collins' interrogation of Iva's husband was straightforward. Filipe was clear that his wife was loyal and committed to the United States, and she insisted that as a couple they had to sacrifice to help the POWs. When asked how often he listened to Iva's broadcasts, Filipe stated that he heard them every day until the end of the war was near and then occasionally.

An unnerving event during Filipe's testimony was that Judge Roche fell asleep twice. Each time, the judge stopped the questioning and made the court reporter read back what had transpired. Collins stared at Roche. The judge dismissively waved to the defense counsel to continue questioning.

The prosecutor stepped forward and started his questioning. "Mr. D'Aquino, so you are mixed-blood Japanese and Portuguese, correct?"

Collins stood. "Objection, Your Honor. The racial status of the witness is not relevant."

"Overruled."

DeWolfe continued. "Is it safe to say that since you grew up and went to school in Japan, you're more Japanese than Portuguese?"

"I'm a Portuguese citizen."

"But you live in Japan, so you must like that country. Now you said that toward the end of the war, you listened to your wife's broadcasts occasionally, correct?"

"Yes."

"So if she made statements about Americans losing ships and sailors being unable to get home, you might have missed that."

Filipe looked at Iva and licked his lips. "I guess, but I know my wife would never say anything like that. I wish the radio recordings weren't destroyed so you could see that never happened."

"But we have no recordings, and you didn't listen every day, so you can't say for sure, Mr. D'Aquino. No further questions."

<hr />

IN THE FOLLOWING DAYS, THE DEFENSE BROUGHT FOR-ward a variety of witnesses. Collins emphasized to the jury that only volunteers who traveled on their own would be testifying for the defense. While the government paid the prosecution's witnesses, the defense wasn't afforded the same treatment.

Kenneth Parkyns was sworn in. Collins started questioning the Australian about his experiences as a POW and the benefit of the smuggled items Iva provided.

DeWolfe objected. "Your Honor, the defense keeps trying to return to this line of questioning that is not relevant to whether the accused committed treason."

Roche leaned forward and stared at the defense counsel. "Sustained. I warned you about this previously, Mr. Collins."

"But Your Honor..."

"No more, Mr. Collins. You are trying my patience. If this witness has nothing more to offer, I suggest you move on before I sanction you."

Collins stared long and hard at the judge and slowly said, "No further questions."

Several service members and ham operators next testified they never heard Iva say anything treasonous. Since there were multiple female radio announcers, none of these witnesses knew how any one of the women could be accurately identified as Tokyo Rose. One especially compelling testimony came from an army radio operator in Alaska who cited his commanding officers saying *Zero Hour* and its music was a real morale booster.

When it came time to get the nineteen depositions from Japan into the record, Collins insisted on reading each one of them word for word. The judge pressured the defense to put them in the record, and the jury could read them later, but Collins dug in his heels, insisting the jury needed to hear them to understand their importance.

Judge Roche was visibly annoyed. "If you insist, Mr. Collins."

The defense counsel started reading the deposition transcript from Ruth Hayakawa in which she made it clear Iva had resisted the Japanese at every opportunity. Several female announcers could be Tokyo Rose, even Ruth herself. Hayakawa finally stated Iva couldn't be Tokyo Rose because of her squeaky voice.

Not two sentences into the deposition, DeWolfe rose. "Objection, Your Honor." No reason was given for the objection.

"Sustained. The jury will ignore that last sentence."

Collins glared at the judge and started reading again. After a few more sentences, DeWolfe again said, "Objection."

"Sustained."

Through each deposition, this dance continued. When Collins asked for clarification, Roche said none was needed and to get on with his reading.

After court that day, Collins spoke to Iva and the

team. "That was a disaster. It's impossible for the jury to fully understand everything in the depositions because of DeWolfe's constant interruptions. The one positive is the lack of clarifications from the judge, for his rulings will be gold if we have to appeal."

"I counted 160 objections he supported during that whole fiasco," Tamba said.

Great, more basis for an appeal. It'll be me tomorrow against that prosecutor and judge.

CHAPTER 33

Iva entered the meeting room on the forty-sixth day of the trial to prepare for the day's session. The defense team greeted her warmly, but it was obvious that everyone felt tense. Coming over and putting his arm on her shoulder, Collins said, "I know this isn't good timing, but you need to know. After his testimony, the FBI grabbed Filipe and put him on a ship back to Japan. That's why he wasn't in court yesterday. He's gone, and despite his requests to say goodbye to you, the FBI packed him off."

Iva dropped her head to the table and started to cry. "They couldn't even wait for the end of the trial." She sobbed. "His visa wasn't up, and then to not even allow a goodbye? Will I ever see him again? They're awful."

Stepping back, Collins said, "We've only got a few minutes, and then you're on the stand. I need you to channel your anger and give me the best performance you can."

Iva continued to cry. "Will I ever see my husband again?"

The door opened, and a court official said, "It's time."

Looking down at his weeping witness, Collins said, "Tell the judge we need a delay."

"He's not going to like that."

"Never mind. I'll go talk to him. Ted, take over here."

Thirty minutes later, Collins returned and said, "We've got to get into the courtroom. Roche was unsympathetic to your situation. I argued as long as I could. I'm sorry, Iva."

Somewhat composed, Iva stood up and said with a deep sigh, "Let's go."

A few minutes later, an emotionally drained Iva was sitting in the witness chair looking out at the packed courtroom. *Look at them. The jackals, especially the press. Raw meat to be had today at the American version of a Roman circus. Here comes Wayne. Come on, time to focus. I don't have the energy, but I must. It's now or never.*

"Mrs. D'Aquino, could you please state your entire name?" Collins said.

———

FOR FOUR DAYS, IVA FACED QUESTIONING BY HER DEFENSE attorney. After gaining initial energy, she faltered by the third session. Instead of a firm and confident voice, Iva seemed confused and halting in her answers.

That night when the defense team met, she was quizzed as to what was going on.

"I'm so tired, and it's hard for me to focus. With all the events we're going over, I'm having trouble keeping dates and events straight in my head. Maybe I'm having a relapse with dysentery since I feel so weak. I thought I was over my sickness after we had to stop the trial a few weeks ago so I could recover. Maybe I'm not going to be able to do what I need to do. I'm sorry."

"Don't worry," Collins said reassuringly. "This is tough, and we'll get you back on track. Whatever is going on, the day after tomorrow DeWolfe will start his cross-examination. You'll need to be at the top of your game for that."

Iva tried to smile, but she felt petrified. If she was struggling this much with her attorney, what would it be like with DeWolfe? Remembering the way the prosecutor had badgered and confused Reyes during his testimony, another wave of dread washed over her.

The next day Iva did a little better, but now the defense team was worried.

THE MORNING OF THE START OF THE PROSECUTION'S cross-examination, Collins said to his client, "Your father wants to talk with you, so we'll meet you in the courtroom."

Jun entered the conference room where the defense prepared and stepped over to embrace his daughter. Since Japanese tradition dictated no physical contact by fathers, Iva was thankful that Jun was different.

"Daddy, I'm scared. It's been so hard the last few days. You've borrowed so much money because of this trial. I don't want to disappoint you during the cross-examination."

"You could never disappoint me, Daughter. It's I who failed you. Do the best you can. I believe what you've said all along. Tell the truth, and everything will turn out okay."

"Do you think Mommy is watching today? I think about her often and how I want to be with you and the others in the Chicago store. I'm tired of being in jail."

"I'm sure Fumi is watching over you today and is proud of you no matter what happens."

The door opened, and Collins stuck his head in. "Time to go."

As Iva closed the door behind her, Jun sat alone and wept, praying for his daughter.

⟵⟶

FEELING SMALL IN THE WITNESS BOX CHAIR, IVA WATCHED DeWolfe approach to stand a few feet in front of her. Staring into her eyes, he said nothing for a moment, obviously trying to intimidate her. "Mrs. D'Aquino, you did not state in 1947 that you were not Portuguese, did you?"

Iva thought for a moment. "May I have that question again?"

DeWolfe said, "Yes, it's hard for you to understand."

"You had a double negative there," Iva said.

The prosecutor leaned toward the witness. "Is the question hard for you to understand?"

Iva thought and said, "I believe my answer is no."

DeWolfe said, "Was that question hard for you to understand?"

The defense counsel stood. "Objection, Your Honor. I submit this questioning is argumentative. You did not lay a foundation, Mr. DeWolfe."

Judge Roche interjected. "The question has been asked and answered. Let's proceed."

DeWolfe returned to Iva. "Was that question hard for you to understand?"

Collins said, "I object to that as argumentative."

Roche replied, "Objection overruled. She may answer."

DeWolfe asked, "Was that hard for you to understand?"

Iva said, "Yes, because I don't know when in 1947."

The prosecutor stared at Iva. "You're supposed to be the one who knows, Mrs. D'Aquino."

Collins stood. "Your honor, I submit that is argumentative."

The judge said nothing as DeWolfe said to Iva in a rising voice, "Was the question hard for you to understand? Answer my question, please."

Iva didn't know what to say.

Collins again said, "Your Honor."

Judge Roche said, "Sit down, Mr. Collins, and the witness will answer the question."

Have I been up here for only ten minutes? I know this was going to be bad, but the prosecutor is really after me. I thought I answered the question, so what do I say now? My hands are sweating.

DEWOLFE WAS ON TO HIS NEXT QUESTIONS. "MRS. D'Aquino, weren't you once a Japanese citizen?"

Remembering her mother recording her birth in the Family Registry of Japan, Iva said, "It's a typical practice of Japanese families in America to record births in Japan, so there's a situation of dual citizenship. My family took my name off that registry after Japan invaded Manchuria, so I'm a citizen of only this country."

"But for a time, you were a citizen of Japan. After you got married, you were a citizen of Portugal, correct?"

"No, I was never a citizen of Portugal. That was an option since my husband is Portuguese, but I never took any action to register."

"It seems to me you must be conflicted in your loyalties with so many options, and once you were in Japan, loyalty to your family there made you support that government. Let's move on."

Iva stammered, "Uh…what? My sole loyalty…"

DeWolfe cut her off. "I have other questions, Mrs. D'Aquino. Please don't interrupt me."

Collins rose. "Objection, Your Honor. Counsel is badgering the witness who only wants to clarify the confusion Mr. DeWolfe is creating."

Judge Roche said, "Objection overruled. Continue, Mr. DeWolfe. The witness is instructed to limit her comments to answering the questions."

TWO DAYS LATER, IVA'S HEAD WAS POUNDING. DEWOLFE just finished reading forty-one statements she supposedly said on air about wives and girlfriends who were cheating on soldiers and sailors back home while also calling US Marines butchers. Although Iva denied each one, the prosecutor challenged her repeatedly, which led to exhaustion. Eventually DeWolfe stated he had one last series of questions, so Iva felt hope as she prayed for this ordeal to be over.

"Let's turn to Charges V and VI, Mrs. D'Aquino. They state that you broadcast statements about the loss of American ships. Do you remember making those remarks?"

Iva felt a rush of adrenaline. Here was the minefield her counsel warned her about. *Concentrate. This could be the make-or-break part of my testimony.*

"I never spoke those words."

"Really? The notes of Mr. Lee and the testimony of several witnesses indicate you did say those words. Are you calling those witnesses liars?"

"I don't know if they're lying. Maybe another female announcer said that and the witnesses were confused."

"It's clear from witnesses that you did speak those words telling American servicemen they'd be orphans because of their loss of ships. You went by the name Orphan Ann, and you've stated in previous testimony that you often called the Allied troops serving in the Pacific orphans. That sounds like you and not someone else. As I've pointed out, every broadcast of *Zero Hour* was nothing but propaganda, and you calling servicemen orphans was part of that propaganda. Your attempt to say you only did entertainment is laughable. Imagine the Japanese government only wanted to make sure enemy soldiers were entertained. Then you say you were forced to do these broadcasts, but no one ever beat you or put a gun to your head. You had a chance to act on your Japanese roots and fit in with a country conducting a cruel war against the United States. As far as the words about lost ships, it's your word against several witnesses. I know who I believe."

DeWolfe stared at Iva as her head swam, confused about what to do or say.

The prosecutor spun on his heels and said, "No further questions."

THE NEXT DAY, IVA CONTINUED TO STRUGGLE AS COLLINS went over points of clarification. Several times he had Iva repeat how the Japanese threatened her as well as deny that she ever spoke about lost ships. When the defense counsel tried to touch upon her heroic efforts to aid POWs, DeWolfe and his incessant objections limited the effectiveness of her testimony.

Taking a deep sigh, Collins stood close to his client. "Mrs. D'Aquino, have you ever wanted to be anything other than a loyal citizen of the United States?"

Sitting up straight, Iva answered in a full voice, "No. I've been nothing but loyal to this country, and I never want to live anywhere else."

Iva's seven days of testimony were finally at an end.

CHAPTER 34

ix days after closing arguments, the parties were back in the courtroom where the jury would receive final instructions from Judge Roche. Before the judge entered the chambers, the prosecuting and defense attorneys came into the courtroom with written copies of the judge's instructions. Dropping the thick stack of paper on the table, Collins leaned in as the entire defense team came close to hear what he had to say. "Look at this, fifty pages of instructions, and a lot of it is garbage. I spent the last hour arguing with Roche about how many of these instructions don't fit the case."

The other attorneys were fingering through the document. Tamba asked, "What's particularly egregious here?"

Collins pointed to a line of text and said, "Roche instructs the jury to pay especially close attention to the testimony of servicemen who claim to have heard Iva speak and how she demoralized them. We showed with every one of them that they couldn't be sure they were even hearing Iva. Roche goes on to discuss intent versus motive. He compares what Iva did—helping the POWs—to someone who wants to feed the poor but steals a car to deliver the food. I told him that theoretical crime doesn't apply. He goes on to say that unless the Japanese physically beat Iva, she has no defense of coercion. This old white man sitting in America decides that threats a single woman experienced in a hostile country are not real. The jury is also instructed to ignore in their deliberations any help she provided to the POWs."

Iva hid her face in her hands as the tears flowed. Seeing his daughter start to cry, Jun came to the rail and tried to reach for her. Bailiff Cole directed him back to his seat.

"All rise. This court is now in session."

IVA LEANED AGAINST HER FATHER AS THEY SAT IN THE bailiff's office while the jury was locked away. The instructions proved even more damning than Collins had indicated. Another directive to the jury was that the testimonies of George Mitsushio and Kenkichi Oki were critically important and should be central in their deliberations. Collins filed his objections to the judge's instructions to get reservations on the record. Press members who were talking in the hallway saw this guidance as proof the judge wanted a conviction.

Iva wished she could disappear and not be part of this anymore. As she knew all too well, she made mistakes in Japan. *What if I had never agreed to that first interview with the reporters? Without Brundidge or Lee stirring the pot later, the army investigation in Japan finding me innocent might have been the end of this. The offer of $2,000 after all the years of deprivation made me blind to Filipe's concerns. Why did I ever agree to go around signing autographs as Tokyo Rose? It seemed just a silly thing at the time, since all the soldiers said Rose kept their morale up* *during the war. Here I am facing prison or worse without a husband to stand by me.*

Burrowing into her father's chest, she said, "I wish I'd done some things differently in Japan, but I don't deserve what's happening to me. I always felt, and you've said the same, tell the truth, and everything will be okay. Well, I stayed loyal to this country and told the truth, and it keeps getting worse. Maybe I should have gone to Portugal with Filipe."

"Daughter, I admit it looks dark, but hopefully the jury will see through the mist and find the truth."

Iva's sister joined them, carrying bags of take-out. "The others went back to the hotel. I brought some food, since it looks like this may be a long night."

Sitting up, Iva said, "I'm not hungry. You two eat."

Jun said, "You need your strength and must not get sick again. Come, let's all eat together."

Hugging her sister and thanking her for being there for the whole trial, Iva said, "I'll try to get something down."

<hr/>

IT WAS ALMOST MIDNIGHT WHEN THE JURY ANNOUNCED it was done for the day and would continue deliberations the next morning. With the jury sequestered for the first time in the trial, the defense team hoped the jury members being locked up away from their families would expedite deliberations. Over the next three days, it became apparent there wouldn't be a quick verdict.

The jury returned several times and asked the judge for clarification about his instructions. Since both the prosecuting and defense teams had to be in attendance for those sessions, Collins explained to the defense team the jury was focusing on one charge: discussing ships. "The other seven vague charges aren't an issue. I can see why the jury is struggling, since Roche's specific instruction directed them to consider that Iva's two managers in Japan testified she said those words. Hopefully, the jury will remember how we shot holes in their testimony."

Iva tried to recall that one broadcast. *Did I say those words? It was near the end of the war. Cousens was sick, and the Japanese army was pushing for more propaganda. There were so many scripts I read in 1944 without being able to make changes. Was I tired that day and didn't catch the importance of those words? I testified I never said those words, but did I?*

The jury returned twice and informed the judge it was hopelessly split. Roche refused to accept a hung jury. The defense team knew that would essentially be an acquittal, since the government wouldn't attempt such a weak prosecution again. The judge repeatedly told the jury that this was too expensive a case for it not to reach a verdict. Collins said to Iva and her father, "The judge says that the cost of the trial should force a verdict rather than the facts determining what the jurors decide. What a court this guy is running. It's clear Roche is on a mission."

In one of the clarification sessions, it was apparent how confused the jury was when the judge responded to one of their questions. It was the afternoon of the fourth day, and the jury had a specific question about intent and motive. Judge Roche said, "You are cautioned not to select a single instruction or portion of instruction alone but to consider all the instructions in determining the issue in this case.

The jury must give uniform consideration to all instructions herein given, consider the whole and every part of them together, and accept such instructions as a correct statement of law involved."

The foreman and jurors looked confused. The foreman started to say something, seemingly struggling for words.

Judge Roche said, "If the jury has no further questions at this time, your deliberations may resume."

Tamba leaned toward the defense team and said, "Anyone got an idea what Roche just said?"

FORTY-FIVE MINUTES LATER, THE DEFENSE TEAM received notice the jury had reached a decision and to assemble in the courtroom. Iva could barely stand as Tamba took her arm and helped her upstairs. In a few minutes, the jury entered. The foreman stood. When asked for the verdict, the foreman looked away from the defense table and said, "Guilty."

A gasp filled the courtroom as Iva slumped in her chair, not surprised at the outcome but overwhelmed in despair. To her right, she heard one of the alternate jurors say, "How could they do that?"

Iva felt the table vibrate as Collins pounded on it. "Guilty without proof," he repeated several times.

Her head spun as she thought about her future. Based upon time already served since being arrested, the defense team had projected it was likely she would get no more than three years. Three more long years before she could be free. Raising her head and turning to look at her family, she saw shock and tears.

CHAPTER 35
1949-1956

One week later, Iva sat in the courtroom for her sentencing. In a few minutes, her fate would be announced. Despite the outrage at the verdict from many around her, including several court officials and much of the press, she was going to stay in jail. She prayed the conventional sentence of a few years was all this terrible judge would impose, but she worried that since he was so one-sided during the trial, he might impose a steeper sentence. Technically it could be death, but could Roche be that extreme?

Collins' team submitted an appeal to declare a mistrial, which Judge Roche rejected out of hand. Now that appeal would be submitted to a lengthy review by the Ninth Circuit Court. As Collins said to the press, "Iva never abandoned the United States. It was her country that abandoned her."

Roche entered the courtroom and said, "In light of the serious nature of treason, I'm sentencing you to ten years imprisonment at the Federal Reformatory for Women and a fine of $10,000. Your US citizenship is forfeited. This hearing is closed." Roche left the bench and disappeared into his chambers.

The courtroom was stunned by the severity of the sentence. Collapsing, Iva felt so empty and numb she couldn't hear her defense team trying to console her. *There's no credit for the past two years I spent locked up. Ten years! How am I going to pay a $10,000 fine? My dad will want to pay it, but he's borrowed so much already. Somehow I'll have to figure out how to pay. He took my citizenship away. Can he do that? All I did to stay loyal during the war, and now I'm not even a citizen.*

CHAPTER 36

The train slowly pulled out of the station on a long cross-country trip to West Virginia. Through the window, Iva saw her father and sister waving. They promised to visit as often as they could but knew how far it was from Chicago to the remote mountains of West Virginia. As she leaned back, Iva thought how similar her next few years were going to be to those in Japan. She was on her own there, and it would be the same in an American prison.

Sitting across from her, his wife next to him, was Bailiff Cole. Since Cole had been with her during the long trial, it was a blessing he volunteered to be the one to take her to prison. Cole hoped inviting his wife to join them on the trip would provide female support for his prisoner. While this would not change the fact that she was on her way to prison, Iva was thankful for this kind gesture.

Right before she boarded the train, Iva had put on a brave face during a press interview and said, "I'll serve my ten years and sleep every night, but can Mitsushio and Oki do the same?" The helplessness and depression Iva felt during the later stages of the trial and sentencing evolved into extreme anger. The more she learned about the jury deliberations and after-the-fact regrets of several of the jurors, the more she struggled to control her emotions.

It turned out the issue of her broadcasting about lost ships was the jury's sole focus. They acquitted her on all other charges. The press reported that three of the jurors were against conviction, because the prosecution did not prove Iva spoke those specific words. Those jurors were worn down by the other nine after long days of intense argument. The majority kept returning to the specific instructions of Roche, citing that Iva must be guilty based upon the testimonies of Mitsushio and Oki. Expecting a mild sentence from the judge, the three hold-outs eventually went along with the majority. Now those three, who included the jury foreman, publicly stated their regret, given the harsh sentence Roche had imposed.

Iva's anger kept returning to the perjured testimonies of Mitsushio and Oki. After the trial, the State Department rewarded them with the right to keep their American citizenship despite having become Japanese citizens at the start of the war. *Since neither of them formally renounced their US citizenship once in Japan, weren't they guilty of treason? How was I rewarded for being loyal?*

Iva appreciated Collins' promise to carry her fight forward. He was already preparing the appeal to the Ninth Circuit, and he tried to buck up her spirits by citing the wealth of material with which he had to work. The attorney was clear it would take some time to put together the necessary documents, and getting on the docket at the appeals court would take months. If the Ninth Circuit upheld Roche, there would be an appeal to the Supreme Court. In the meantime, Iva knew there were more years of prison ahead.

Tamba promised if the appeals failed, he'd take the lead to apply for a presidential pardon. Before she left for prison, he said, "There's ample evidence for a pardon since this trial was a travesty of justice, but presidential pardons are as much about politics as justice, so there are no guarantees." Iva remembered laughing to herself. *I'm thankful for his efforts, but look where politics has gotten me.* She stretched her tired muscles and came back to the present.

Bailiff Cole smiled. "We brought crossword puzzles, and my wife made some cookies. Let us know if you want either. I took the liberty of contacting your brother. When we change trains in Chicago, he'll meet us. I'm not supposed to do this, but I'll leave you alone with him so you can visit. It's only a few hours, but it's the best I can do."

Iva smiled at this kind man. "You both are so thoughtful, and I'm sure at some point I'll take you up on the offer of cookies. For now, I want to look out the window and do some thinking."

Iva turned to the window and saw her reflection. She watched a single tear trickle down her cheek.

CHAPTER 37

The automobile ride from the train station to the prison wound through the Allegheny Mountains of West Virginia. It was November, and there was a distinct chill in the air and few leaves remaining on the trees. Iva imagined it would be scenic come spring when everything was in bloom but doubted there'd be any field trips to take in the sights.

She fought a feeling of dread, as her companions would soon turn her over to the prison authorities. Iva hoped what Bailiff Cole said was correct: "This is the first federal prison built solely for women with a mission of rehabilitation. If you must go to jail, this is the place you want." Feeling she was a prison expert with all the facilities she occupied over the years, she wished she didn't have to test his opinion.

The driver from the prison turned onto a quiet road, and Iva spied the gate to Alderson Prison. Once in front of the main administration building, she stepped out of the car and was greeted by several matrons who started explaining the administrative process she would go through.

On the other side of the vehicle, Cole was handing paperwork to another official. They chatted while looking at her. In a minute, Cole and his wife came around to say goodbye and wish her well. Cole said, "The staff here is already disappointed. They expected a glamorous and seductive woman to show up in furs, pearls, and high heels. Your worn two-piece suit has thrown them for a loop."

"They've been reading too many of those sensational news stories about me."

Cole and his wife laughed as they gave Iva a final hug. The bailiff said, "Now they get to know the real Iva. Time for us to go. It's been wonderful spending time with you even under these conditions. You're a special person and don't deserve what's happened to you. We wish you the best for your time here and the rest of your life when you're released."

Iva was hustled out of the cold wind and into the central offices. The now-familiar process of paperwork, photographs, fingerprints, medical exams, issuing of prison wear, and signing of forms started. Several hours later, the prison warden said, "We're ready to take you to your cottage if you have everything you need."

"My cottage? Do you mean I won't be in a big building with rows of cells?"

"Not unless there are disciplinary issues and you need to be moved. Your history shows no violence, so we start you in cottages where most prisoners live."

"How many share the cottage?"

"Nineteen, although everyone has a separate room. We've got a little over three hundred prisoners now, and our capacity is five hundred. Your cottage, number seven, shares a common bathroom."

Soon Iva was in her tiny room, and for the first time in several years, she felt hopeful. The conditions were superior to any prison she'd experienced to date. It was simple with a bed, desk, bureau, and chair. If she could get some material and make curtains, perhaps even a rug or two, this could be cozy. She committed to herself not to violate any rules and risk being relocated. As she started to unpack her few things, she couldn't help but think of that morning on the pier at Yokohama with her thirty trunks and cases. She shook her head in sadness.

There was a knock at the door. Two prisoners stood there. One of the women said, "Hi. You're new and famous, so we wanted to meet you. I'm Elly, and this is Sarah. We heard you're Tokyo Rose, but that can't be. You don't seem glamorous, and you're so small."

"I've been getting that comment since I got here. It's cold out there. Do you want to come in?"

Sarah said, "You just got here and should get settled first."

Elly interrupted. "Heck, I'll come in. She has all the time in the world to unpack."

The women sat on the bed as Iva pulled her chair over. Smiling at them, she said, "I'm Iva. How long have you been here, and is it okay to walk around and visit other prisoners?"

Elly said, "It is during certain hours. Things are pretty loose. I've been here for a little over a year, and Sarah's new."

Looking down, Iva noticed Elly was barefoot. "Excuse me for asking, but isn't it too cold to be walking around barefoot?"

Laughing, Elly said, "Heck, I never wore shoes in my life until I got here. I was raised in the mountains. We're both in here for runnin' moonshine. If you're not glamorous, how can you be Tokyo Rose?"

"Well, that's a bit of a story. Do you have some time?"

"A little over a year." The three women laughed.

Before Iva could start to explain, there was a sharp knock on the door. The door opened, and a tall, formidable-looking woman stepped inside. Elly and Sarah jumped up almost at attention. Iva saw that and decided to follow suit.

"I'm Muriel Houchins, your cottage warder for this residence." Turning to Iva's guests, she said, "What are you doing here? Are your rooms in order? Maybe you ought to get there, as I'll come by for an inspection after I'm done here."

"Yes, ma'am," the women said as they rushed out the door.

Closing the door behind them, Houchins turned back to Iva. "They explain what a cottage warder is during your orientation?"

"A little bit."

Houchins took a couple of steps forward and was next to Iva. "From now on, it's a little bit *ma'am*. Understand?"

"Yes, ma'am."

Looking Iva up and down, the warder quietly said, "So you're the traitor. You should know I was in the army during the war, and I find what you did to aid the enemy despicable. When I got you assigned to my cottage, I couldn't have been happier. Do you like this cozy room? Well, mess up once, and you'll be in a real cell so fast it'll make your head spin."

Iva saw the vein in Houchins' neck standing out. The woman was almost out of control. Iva told herself to be quiet but was worried, knowing this was someone she was going to have to deal with.

"You don't seem so high and mighty now, Iva. Smart to keep your mouth shut. Make sure that becomes a habit. We have a few rules and assignments to go over, but that'll come later. Now we need ice cream for dinner, and you're going to make it. Get your jacket, and let me introduce you to your new friend, the ice cream maker."

Putting on her thin coat from California, Iva followed her warder outside to an area where a machine several feet tall stood. Two other prisoners stood there. Houchens barked to them, "Have you got all the ingredients loaded including the rock salt?"

"Yes, ma'am," one said.

"Good. You two can go now."

The prisoners scurried off as the warder turned to Iva. "Get to work. It should take about two hours of cranking. The prison is counting on dessert tonight."

Houchins walked away. Feeling the cold wind blow through her thin jacket, Iva thought about running back to her room to get more clothes, but she saw the light would soon fade, and she didn't want to aggravate her warder. With the ingredients loaded, she reached up to the big crank. Giving a pull with all her strength, she got the handle down but then had to push with all her strength to get it back up.

Eventually, Iva got into a rhythm, though she was quickly fatigued. Her shoulders started to cramp, begging for a break. After stopping once to rest, she concluded it was more work getting started again than the rest was worth. Determined to not get off on the wrong foot with Houchins, Iva closed her eyes to her pain and cranked for all she was worth.

OUT OF THE DUSK, HOUCHINS APPEARED. "HOW'S IT going, traitor? Do we have dessert yet?"

Iva stopped her cranking and stood shaking with exhaustion. Houchins lifted the top of the container and inserted a finger to sample the ice cream. After tasting it, the warder turned and smiled at Iva. "Good job. This is delicious. You can head back to your room and get cleaned up for dinner. This batch is good. I think you'll churn tomorrow's ice cream as well. In fact, plan on doing this every day along with your job in the storehouse that starts tomorrow. We're going to find out how strong you are. Any questions?"

"No, ma'am." Iva turned and struggled to walk. Looking back at her warder, she said, "I'm pretty tired and may skip dinner to rest, ma'am."

"No, you won't, Iva. We take a count at dinner, so you be there. Don't want to violate a rule your first day, right? Besides, you need to eat to keep up your strength for what I have planned for you."

HOUCHINS WAS NOT EXAGGERATING ABOUT IVA GETTING manual work. The next day, she learned what a tough job her assignment to the prison storehouse was. It was the central area where supplies for the camp were processed, stored, and distributed. It was easily the most physically challenging job in the prison because of the heavy lifting, and when added to the daily ice cream assignment, Iva struggled.

Keep going. I can do this. If I show Houchins I'll do whatever she wants, maybe she'll lighten up. Besides, I'm starting to develop muscles in my shoulders, since the ice cream making is getting easier.

Other prisoners and Miss Smithson, the thin, immaculately groomed storehouse supervisor, recognized Iva's unfair treatment. At the end of her first week, Smithson came over to Iva, who was struggling to move heavy boxes, and said, "Put that down. I want to chat with you in my office. Please follow me."

Iva was glad for the break, although she dreaded what this official might be planning.

Once seated, Smithson asked, "You any good with math? Your file said you went to college, so you should be able to work with numbers. Right?"

Iva drew in a quick breath of hope. "Sure, I'm good with numbers. What do you need?"

Looking down at the stacks of paper on her desk, Smithson said, "Well, I'm not very good with math and tracking, so this place is a mess. I need someone who can sort this all out. Do you want to give it a try?"

"Sure. If you show me the basics and what you want to organize, I'll sort it out."

"Good. Pull your chair up next to me, and let's start looking at this chaos."

As Iva took in the cluttered papers listing supplies, bills, due dates, and other critical information, she relished this turn of events. *Thank goodness for Smithson needing help. How long can I make this assignment last?*

THE NEXT DAY, IVA WAS SITTING AT A SMALL DESK IN THE corner of Smithson's office, trying to bring order to the piles of paper. Through the closed door, she heard two people arguing. Through the glass window in the door, she saw Smithson and Houchins toe to toe, going back and forth. Turning back to her work, Iva strained to hear what the women were saying, but it was muffled by the door.

Suddenly it was quiet, and Smithson stormed into the office, slamming the door behind her. As the supervisor collapsed into her office chair, Iva heard Smithson say with exasperation, "That Houchins. Who in the hell does she think she is to tell me how to do my job? She may have pulled strings to get you assigned here, but this is my turf. If I want you to do paperwork, you'll do what I say."

Iva stayed quiet.

"That woman has it out for you, Iva. She's probably on her way to your room right now to do a surprise inspection. I hope everything is neat and clean there, your floor waxed and furniture dusted."

"That shouldn't be a problem, ma'am."

"Good. You're in prison for a reason, and I don't care what that is. It's not fair that anyone is singled out for special punishment, although I think you might be making ice cream for a while."

Iva smiled. "I'll do what she makes me do. I only want to get along and get out of here without any problems as soon as possible."

"That's the right approach. How are things going over there with that mess I gave you?"

"Not bad. I've got a few questions but also a few ideas on how to get this organized. Is now a good time to go over this?"

"You already have some ideas? If you can get that sorted out so I can show my boss, maybe I'll stick my nose into Houchins' business and see about getting you out of ice cream duty."

⌒

SEVERAL MONTHS LATER, IVA WAS SITTING AT HER corner desk feeling bored. Now that the information for all aspects of the storehouse was organized, it was just a matter of maintaining the system and staying on top of the paperwork. The job was straightforward, and she was regularly asking for additional duties.

Later that morning, Smithson entered the office and closed the door behind her. It was apparent that her supervisor was agitated, so Iva said nothing. Smithson said, "My big mouth got me in trouble. I was bragging to the warden how well you have this place organized and how smart you are. It turns out there's a brand-new computer project that I don't understand. It's going to cover the entire prison, and they need someone to organize that and put information into punch cards, so now I'm going to lose you."

Iva was excited about a new assignment but didn't want to let Smithson know she would be happy to move on. "I don't know anything about computers, ma'am. I've read about them in the newspaper, but that's all. I don't know if I'd be any good at that."

Smithson gave a little laugh. "You're so sharp that it won't be a problem. Besides, it's a done deal. I convinced the warden I need you for another week to train someone, although we might want to train a couple of people since you're doing so much. Got any ideas on who might be candidates?"

"I hate to leave you, ma'am. You've been good to me, especially getting me out of making ice cream. Now I can finally enjoy dessert. How about Joanne as a trainee? She's a college graduate and always asking me what I'm doing. Mary Ellen has a similar background and was teaching when she was prosecuted as a communist. What do you think of those two?"

"Good suggestions. Go get them, and let's start talking."

CHAPTER 38

W alking back to her cottage on a Friday afternoon, Iva took in the view from the hilltop prison camp. With springtime in full bloom, the mountains of West Virginia were as beautiful as she'd hoped.

She was finishing her latest day on the federal prison census coding project, and her brain was slowly clearing from another day of organizing data on all the Alderson prisoners. While initially challenging like the storehouse, she had quickly developed a system. The bulk of the project was entering data on punch cards and making sure the information was correct. Over forty-six thousand individual information bundles needed to be coded and integrated. The work was tedious and complex, but Iva loved it for its challenge and the way it made time fly. Once prison officials recognized her capabilities, Iva was soon leading a small team.

Entering data on all the prisoners was fascinating, since it required her to review everyone's prison file. Iva learned there was no one stereotype for prisoners here. Backgrounds ranged from moonshiners to prostitutes and communist sympathizers. Recently the famous blues singer Billie Holiday had been released after serving a sentence on drug charges.

With the weekend ahead, Iva looked forward to her free hours. The weekdays were full of work responsibilities and other duties, but evenings and weekends were largely unstructured. During these off hours, there were many education programs or activities to choose from, and Iva was trying out several of them. She especially enjoyed attending Catholic mass. With some study, she learned enough Latin that the priest offered to train her to become his altar girl. She accepted. Thinking back to her first experiences joining the church, she wondered what Father Kraus and Filipe would think about her assisting in a mass.

Iva also took up weaving, and soon her room was covered with rugs. Another prisoner helped her sew the drapes she envisioned on her first day. With the threat of surprise visits from Warder Houchins, Iva always made sure her room was spotless. Prison administrators now brought visitors first to Iva's room, since it was a showplace. Her room was also a refuge where Iva cherished time alone reading. The prison library was well stocked, and her father paid for a subscription to the *Chicago Tribune*, so she was on top of current events.

Houchins' harassment dropped off, especially after the start of the data project. A message had been conveyed to use a lighter touch with Iva. Even though her warder still carried feelings against Iva, things settled into an uneasy truce. Iva still was often assigned to clean the bathroom used by all the women, but that beat ice cream duty.

The next morning, there was a knock on the door, and a dark-haired prisoner Iva had seen in the dining room stood before her. "I'm Mildred Gillars, but I bet you already know who I am."

"You're Axis Sally."

"Yes, and you're Tokyo Rose. Do you play cards?"

"No, not really. Why?"

"I need a bridge partner, and with so many dumbshits around here, I can't find anyone who can keep up with me. By now, we all know you're probably the smartest gal in this prison. I'll teach you how to play, and then we'll kick everyone's ass. Are you willing to give it a try?"

Iva thought for a minute. "Okay, I'm game."

Mildred smiled. "Good. You got some time now so I can start to show you the basics?"

"Sure. Come on in."

The women sat down. As Mildred pulled out a deck of cards, she said, "One thing. I don't ask you about what you did during the war and what happened in your trial, and you don't ask me about my experiences or my treason trial. Deal?"

"Fair enough."

"All right. In bridge, there are four players…"

⌒

OVER TIME, IVA'S ROOM BECAME A GATHERING POINT FOR many prisoners. While she sometimes wished for more quiet hours, the growing reliance of her fellow inmates for guidance and support was moving. It was not unusual at any one time to have a couple of women working on their hair or someone studying basic reading lessons in her tiny room while she sat at her desk writing letters home or to lawyers for those who couldn't read. Iva joined in the softball games once the good weather appeared but decided the rough play, which many times resulted in broken bones, made it wiser to sit on the sidelines and assist with first aid.

Early in the second year of the coding project, the warden of the prison surprised Iva at her job. "Sorry to interrupt, but there's a request from our chief medical officer to have you transferred to work in the hospital. You've done great here, but with the team you developed and the fact that the project is almost complete, might you be interested in a change?"

Iva said, "I'd love to learn more about it, sir. I like developing new skills."

"I thought you'd be open to this opportunity. You're a smart woman and fitting in well. Keep up the good work, and when the opportunity for parole comes up in a few years, I'll certainly be supportive. Why don't you head over to the hospital now and chat with Dr. Compton? Your supervisor here is aware of this development and, while not pleased to lose you, wants the best for you."

"Thank you, sir. I'll get over there right now."

A MONTH LATER, IVA WAS THE SECRETARY TO THE PRISon's doctor. Within a short time, she was running all aspects of the medical office. Her duties included not only secretarial duties but gathering information for monthly reports, maintaining patient records, and ordering and tracking medical supplies. Iva approached the gray-haired Dr. Compton to ask if she could start to assist in tests using some of the medical equipment. "I know you get busy and backed up, Doctor. Teach me how to do the tests, and then you only have to read the results. I promise

I won't let the office work fall behind. I have a real interest here and know I can do more. Back at UCLA, I dreamed of going to medical school, but that never worked out. This might be my chance to follow my passion and work in medicine."

Compton smiled. "You're already doing much more than what I intended. If you promise not to let the office systems slip, I'm willing to give you a chance. This afternoon we're doing an electrocardiogram. Join me, and we'll see how that goes."

———

Beginning with the EKG that afternoon, Iva's skills in medicine grew rapidly. Besides conducting electrocardiograms by herself, she began running the fluoroscope and x-ray machines. Next she was drawing blood and analyzing the tests. Compton asked her to scrub up for surgery, and while she was not the assisting nurse, Iva would count sponges, get needed supplies, and do other tasks. Eventually she assisted in several births for prisoners who entered the prison pregnant. The prison pharmacist watched what Iva was doing and started asking for help. Not surprisingly, Iva was soon dispensing medications.

Late one afternoon, Compton was packing up for a three-day trip to a medical conference. "Looks like you've got everything under control here, Iva. You know who to call if there's an emergency. By the way, good work getting blood from that drug abuser who came in today. I couldn't find a vein to tap into, but you were able to get it done. How did you manage that?"

"I discovered that drug users could not reach behind their knees to shoot up, so that's where I managed to find a vein."

"Creative. I'll have to remember that trick. All right, see you in a couple of days."

———

THE NEXT DAY, AS IVA WAS WRAPPING UP HER WORK AT the hospital, Roxie Shelton, one of the medical assistants, came in. A distraught black woman suffering terribly from an infected tooth was with her. Roxy said, "The doc is gone, and this poor woman needs help. What can we do?"

"Let's get her in the dentist's chair and see if I can give her some oil of cloves to relieve the pain."

After applying the cloves, there was no relief for the patient. The woman repeatedly begged Iva to pull the tooth.

Iva said, "I can't do that, since I'm not certified. It's against the rules and would get me in a lot of trouble."

Roxy said, "You know how to do it. You've assisted many times in pulling teeth. We promise to keep it quiet. You've got to help her. It's too late to call the backup doc, and this woman cannot stand another night of this pain."

Iva struggled with what to do. *If I contact anyone in the administration, they will say follow the rules and let this woman suffer, since it's too late to call the backup doctor for a simple tooth issue. The extraction procedure is straightforward and shouldn't be difficult. There's always the possibility of complications, and the patient would be in more trouble, but again, that's a slight chance. If I do this, there's no way to keep it confidential. If nothing else, this woman's warder will see she's better. I promised myself not to break any rules that could threaten my parole, but it's obvious this patient is truly suffering.* Looking at the patient, Iva said, "All right. Let me get what I need. Do you promise not to talk about this?"

Both women nodded. A short time later, the infected tooth was wrapped in gauze and given to the relieved woman. Iva showed her how to clean and pack the site and sent her back to her quarters.

When Compton returned from the conference, Iva took him aside and told him the whole story. "I haven't heard from anyone about what I did, but I believe it's only a matter of time. It's better you know, Doctor."

"Get the woman you treated in here so I can check her out. I can't condone your actions, but I understand why you did it. Promise me you won't do that again."

"I promise, Doctor."

A COUPLE DAYS LATER, HOUCHINS CONFRONTED IVA. "Well, you've stepped in it now. The amazing woman who does everything perfectly goes ahead and conducts a medical operation without a doctor present. That's going to kill any hope you have for an early release. The disciplinary board hearing is tomorrow at 2:00 p.m. I'll be there to watch the show."

THE NEXT AFTERNOON, IVA STOOD IN FRONT OF THE three-member disciplinary board as the charges against her were read. What hurt was that Compton would not attend the hearing, saying he was busy. Since Iva had gotten herself into this mess, she would have to stand alone. Sitting off to the side, Muriel Houchins looked like she was enjoying herself.

Iva explained the incident and what she did. She was relieved there were no outbursts or criticism directed at her, and she noticed two of the board members smiling. The board chair asked, "Do we have any witnesses today?" After a pause, the chair continued. "I have two written statements that I will summarize. The first is from the patient in this case who requests clemency for Mrs. D'Aquino. If not for her swift action, the patient would have suffered needlessly. The second is from Dr. Compton, who could not be here."

I'm in for it now. Compton didn't want to criticize me to my face and instead wrote a letter.

The chair summarized the letter. "Dr. Compton was out of town at the time of the emergency, and since the patient appeared late in the day, calling medical backup for a dental problem was not possible. Mrs. D'Aquino is aware she violated standard practice in the hospital and has promised never to do it again. The doctor asks that we consider the extenuating circumstances in considering our decision. Dr. Compton added a postscript to his statement. Upon his return and examination of the patient, it was clear the procedure was completed perfectly and as well as any professional dentist could have done."

Iva drew a huge sigh of relief. The board members excused themselves to consider what action should be taken.

The panel returned after ten minutes, and the chairman spoke to Iva. "This is a serious breach of prison and hospital rules and a medical risk you weren't qualified to undertake. You're cautioned never to do anything like this again. We've determined to add time to your sentence, which must be served before you can be released. That additional time to your sentence shall be two days." The chair smiled. "You're dismissed."

Turning to leave, Iva saw an unhappy Warder Houchins. *I'd better hustle back to my room and get ready for a surprise inspection.*

CHAPTER 39

I n late 1954, Iva had one of the family visits she so enjoyed. Despite the driving distance from Chicago to the prison, her father and one or more of her siblings had visited almost monthly, and this month Fred drove her father. After greeting his daughter, Jun said, "Your brother is a much better driver than you, Iva. I don't have to worry about arriving dead. Once we get you home, he will teach you better driving habits."

Iva laughed, remembering their wonderful trips after college up the West Coast to Seattle when Iva drove Jun to help his former boss. Now it seemed so long ago and from a different world.

Her brother and father were admiring the wallet Iva made for Jun in her leathermaking class. This was one of the things she was selling outside the prison. At the warden's encouragement, Iva had submitted several leather products to the West Virginia State Fair and won three blue ribbons and a second place. Now there was a steady stream of orders for her leather bags, which she sold for $25 apiece.

Looking at her father as he fingered his new wallet, she saw a tear in his eye. Now in his seventies, Jun looked frail compared to the father who badgered her on those long-ago drives. Her brother now managed the three family stores in Chicago, and he was the spitting image of a younger Jun. *I wonder how I look to them, since time spares no one.*

Fred addressed her. "Iva, you don't look well. You've lost weight, and look at you, sweating while sitting in this cool temperature. Have you seen a doctor?"

Iva had been feeling terrible over the past few weeks, and when alone in the infirmary, she gave herself some tests. Besides losing weight for several weeks, her heart rate was averaging 136 beats per minute. "I'm okay. Maybe coming down with flu or something."

Jun put his hand on his daughter's arm. "Iva, you're not well. Something is wrong. You must promise us to see a doctor and find out what's going on."

She knew arguing was useless. "I promise."

Several days later, she learned she was suffering from a hyperactive thyroid. She was down to seventy pounds, so Dr. Compton ordered her to eat five thousand calories a day including a milkshake delivered in the middle of the night to keep her stable.

Over time, she gained some of her weight back. When Jun learned about her condition, he told his daughter he'd arranged for the University of Chicago to treat her once she was released.

The years slowly rolled by, and in 1955, Iva had her first hearing for early release. Word got out to the press, and there was a round of news stories about the traitor not serving her full sentence. It was with sadness she learned release would not be this year, but with her sparkling record, the parole board said she'd likely earn release in 1956.

Iva worried about returning home, since her family told her how the press harassed them about her parole hearing. She realized that her hope to silently fade from the public spotlight was never going to be achieved.

CHAPTER 40

The rest of 1955 brought three streams of bad news. Wayne Collins' petitions had failed. The Supreme Court's ruling closed the last appeals option. Iva's attorney wondered what role Tom Clark, the former attorney general who had insisted that she be tried, played as a new associate justice on the high court. In the court's opinion, Justice William Douglas issued a minority statement that Iva's conviction and appeal failures appeared more politically based than legally compelling. The minority opinion was small consolation as Iva read Collins' letter.

Earlier in 1952, Tamba filed a request for a presidential pardon with the incoming Dwight Eisenhower. There was never a response from the White House no matter how many times the attorney tried to get clarification. In 1955, Tamba wrote to Iva that it was apparent this president would not be taking any action on her behalf.

The final blow of the year was no longer getting letters from Filipe. Since Iva was in West Virginia, her husband wrote monthly. Recently the letters were more sporadic, culminating in a final letter in which Filipe said he was living with another woman who could take care of him the way Iva once had. Given the circumstances and Iva's clear, continued commitment to living with her family after release, Filipe wrote that he had to move on. As Catholics, they were supposed to remain married for life, but Filipe said he might propose divorce in the future depending on how his new relationship progressed.

Not surprised by this development, Iva carried Filipe's letter around for a week, taking it out often and thinking about what she wanted to say to her husband. One night, she took up her pen.

Dear Fil, It is with great sadness that I read your latest letter. When I look past my feelings, I recognize it's right for you, and I must be supportive. All those years in Japan, you stood by me, often in circumstances that were made more difficult because of the choices I made. I want to thank you for being there when I needed someone more than ever in my life. It was not easy for you, and for that, you will always be the love of my life.

Life has shown me how it can be full of unexpected twists and turns, and with my need to be in America, we never can be together again. I'm happy that you found someone to share your life with, and I wish only the best for the two of you. While the Catholic Church may not condone divorce, I will not contest any action you take on that front.

Please give all my love and thanks to your mother and father for their kindness and support. Thanks again for being there when I needed you most.

Love, Iva

THE PAROLE HEARING HELD IN EARLY 1956 WAS SHORT, AND the feedback was positive. Iva would be paroled on January 28.

CHAPTER 41
1956-1978

On the morning of the big day, Iva was taken from her cottage in the dark at 4:00 a.m. for the planned release at 6:15. The early hour had been selected to minimize press attention, but outside the prison, more than a hundred members of the media gathered. The new plan was to hold a brief press conference on prison grounds and then for Iva's family to drive her to Chicago.

Iva felt the fresh snow crunch beneath her feet. She breathed in the cold mountain air and took in her surroundings one last time.

She had slept little the night before. There were many curfew violations as a steady stream of prisoners came by to say thanks and wish her well. While Iva wanted above all to return to her family, more than once she broke down and cried while saying goodbye to the parade of special persons who made up her prison family. Each promised to stay in touch. She wondered how likely that was. Warder Houchins allowed the curfew violations.

Two days earlier, Iva had been invited to the matron's private apartment. Nervous, she soon relaxed as the women settled into rocking chairs with tea.

"Iva, I want to apologize for my behavior, especially during your early days here. As a former soldier, I was hurt by your actions in Japan. Once you got here, I was determined to make you suffer. I learned over the years what an honest and giving woman you are. So many prisoners have benefited from your help. I don't know everything you went through during the war, but now all I see is a good person. Can you forgive me?"

Stunned by the request, Iva reached over and took her jailer's hand. "Of course I forgive you. All that's in the past." After a pause, Iva said, "Could I ask a favor for something in the years to come?"

"If I can, Iva. What is it?"

"Would you mind exchanging Christmas cards so we can stay in touch? I want us to be friends."

"I'd love that. Thank you for asking."

Another special goodbye was with Mildred Gillars, who attempted to be gruff and say all that mattered was there would be bad bridge without Iva. Not surprisingly, Iva had become quite the card player, and it was rare that the pair lost. Gillars had another eight years on her sentence, reflecting the clear treason she committed for the Nazis. Iva gave Mildred a special rug and bag as thanks for the many happy hours spent at the card table.

When Iva entered a conference room in the administration building, she discovered that Inez had come from Arizona along with Jun and Fred. Embracing her youngest sister, Iva said, "Thank you for coming. It's so far for you to travel."

"Sister, I apologize for not being here sooner. My life has been so crazy, but that's no excuse. The opportunity to see you freed after all this time is something I couldn't miss."

Jun stepped in. "You two will have lots of time to chat in the car. Now we must plan how to get away from all those press guys. Let me introduce Captain Tony Campioli of the Chicago Police Department, and this is Zip, one of his detectives. To avoid those jackals forming a caravan behind our car and harassing us all the way to Chicago, Tony has a plan."

"It's nice to meet you, Iva," said Campioli. "Your dad has told me all about you. Zip and I are here to make sure we get you safely home and with a minimum of hassle. Here's what we're going to do."

THE WARDEN AGREED TO THE PLAN THE DETECTIVES proposed and went outside to announce there would be a brief press conference. Iva would make a statement and depart with two security guards who would drive her back to Chicago.

A few minutes later, Iva stepped out of the administration building with a Chicago policeman on either side. As she walked up to the microphone, flashbulbs fired and disoriented her. Holding for silence until the press stopped yelling questions, she said, "I'm pleased to be released today and want to return to a quiet life with my family. I never did anything wrong and nothing to harm my country, the United States. All I ask is for a chance to be left alone. I won't take any questions at this time." She stepped away from the microphone as the press again hurled questions her way.

Walking with the burly policemen, she was led around the corner and out of sight to a waiting car. In a few minutes, a black sedan roared out from around the corner. The press saw one of her security guards at the wheel and the second in the back seat next to a figure covered by a blanket. Rushing to their vehicles, they formed a parade of cars that chased Iva's automobile.

Inside the administration building, next to the side door that Iva had slipped through, the prison staff congratulated Jun on his planning. Fred said, "Let's start to load up. There's no telling how quickly the press will figure out they're chasing nothing but Tony and Zip. Dad and I mapped out a roundabout way home that will take longer but minimize the chance we're spotted."

Once in their car and away from the prison and after the latest family news was shared, Iva said, "I've some bad news. Last night an Immigration and Naturalization Agent showed up with an order for me to leave the country in thirty days or be forcefully deported."

"Those bastards," Fred murmured.

"Those are the same words Wayne used. Since the warden was as shocked as I was, he let me call my attorney. After Wayne talked to the immigration agent, he told me to sign the receipt for the paperwork so that I could get out of jail on schedule. In the meantime, he'll start work to get the deportation order canceled. Wayne indicated there's another case the Supreme Court will hear soon that should apply to my situation and make clear that this type of order is unlawful, so not to worry. How can I not worry? No matter what I do, the government is out to get me."

Jun said, "Daughter, the important thing is we're together again, so nothing can spoil this day. If Wayne said he'll take care of it and not to worry, we should relax."

It was quiet as everyone in the car thought about Jun's words, but everyone was hoping that Collins did better with this issue than he ultimately did at the trial.

CHAPTER 42

I n Chicago, Iva purposely stayed out of public view in an apartment building her father owned. She didn't visit the family stores, since the press had public opinion stirred up against her. The day after her release, the headline in the *Chicago Tribune* read "Tokyo Rose Quits Jail—Shows No Repentance." Within days, letters started to arrive at the Toguri Mercantile stores from around the country saying awful things and, in some cases, threatening Iva. The detectives who helped Iva escape the press in West Virginia visited her often, and a police car was often parked outside her building to discourage anyone who wanted to do more than write letters. *I've traded one prison for another.*

As the weeks passed, the only outing was her required monthly check in with her parole officer. For those trips, she wore clothing that helped obscure her face. If available, one of the detectives accompanied her. The parole officer himself was not supportive and kept badgering Iva about why she didn't leave the country rather than pursuing legal action to stay. Every time she left his office, Iva felt a wave of relief.

Collins was still working her case, and a judge granted a stay from immediate deportation. Since the appeal would be heard in San Francisco, Iva would travel to and live in her attorney's house in Oakland for the duration of the proceedings.

Once she arrived, Iva was warmly greeted by the entire Collins family, including Wayne Jr., who was eleven. She and the young Collins hit it off, and she spent many nights helping the boy with his homework, especially math. Soon she was also working in her attorney's office as a receptionist and secretary to keep busy. Just like her early days in the prison storehouse, Iva found an organizational mess that kept her more than occupied. Lying in bed at night, she often reflected on the variety of jobs that had come her way under extenuating circumstances.

The Supreme Court ruled in the case Collins said would likely apply to Iva. It involved a soldier during the war who deserted for one day but then voluntarily returned to his unit. The United States' attempt to take away the soldier's citizenship and deport him was ruled cruel and unusual punishment by the high court. Collins clapped his hands as he handed her a copy of the ruling and repeated what she had heard often during the trial. "We got 'em now."

To Collins, there was now a clear precedent regarding Iva's case, but the government dug in attempting to deport her. Despite repeated rebuffs from the courts against the Justice Department filings, it wasn't until July that the federal attorneys admitted defeat. Iva's ability to stay in the United States was secured, but Collins said, "I recommend that you not test the Immigration Service by traveling outside the United States, even to Canada. While the courts have ruled that the government cannot take away your right to citizenship, I doubt they'll ever issue you a passport. In a sense, you're a second-class citizen."

"Why do they keep after me?"

"I think the main reason is there was misconduct on the part of the government during your trial. They'll do anything to make you go away and not be a threat in the future about how you were treated. Did you know DeWolfe announced his retirement shortly after you were released?"

"No, I didn't. Do you think it might be DeWolfe is worried about the fallout from my trial?"

"I wouldn't doubt it, but there are many others in the Justice Department who want you to go away because their fingerprints are on your case."

"I guess that makes sense, but what they may try in the future worries me. What about the $10,000 fine, Wayne?"

"That'll have to be paid. Sorry, I couldn't get that forgiven."

Iva knew she needed to pay that off somehow. *My dad is so old now I can't ask him for the money. I guess it'll be time for me to go to work in the stores when things calm down with the press.*

When the day came for Iva to say goodbye to the Collins family, young Wayne and his mother laughed, saying his father would suffer now, since his office was finally well organized. The attorney took the ribbing well and tearfully gave Iva a final toast. "To the most courageous and loyal woman I know even if our government doesn't recognize that."

Iva's last hug was for Wayne Jr. As he stepped back, the boy said, "I'm going to grow up and be a lawyer like my dad and help people like you."

Iva smiled. "If you do, I know you'll be a fine attorney."

CHAPTER 43

ack in Chicago, life calmed down. Throwing herself into work at the family stores, Iva averaged fourteen-hour days. With her father's role limited because of his age and the health issues that plagued her brother, Iva was soon managing all of the businesses and investments. With a dedicated customer base and crowded aisles, she was soon considering expansion.

One day while meeting with the family attorney, the lawyer shared something her father once said. Jun offered that fate mixed up his children. Though the oldest son who by tradition should have gravitated to assuming management of the businesses, Fred never liked that work and was saddled with poor health. In contrast, his daughter, who never fell into a traditional Japanese woman's role, showed not only the aptitude but interest and commitment to the business.

Hearing this, Iva smiled. *What a strange journey life can be. Maybe I was destined to be trapped in Japan to develop my creative skills to survive. Many of the lessons I learned can be applied to business and taking care of my family. Fate has finally put me in the right place at the right time.*

In her second-floor office in the largest of the stores, the photographs that Iva kept on her desk meant the world to her. One was of her father, and another was of her brother and sisters. The third was of Charles Cousens. *Here is the man who gave me a purpose in Japan by helping the POWs. He never abandoned me and traveled from Australia to try and help me. He told me never to be bitter about my fate but to embrace it and learn from whatever experience was at hand. Knowing I'll probably never see him again hurts.*

She studied her father's picture. Jun seemed to grow older every day, although he fought slowing down and continued to work in the Japanese American community. Fred was the one who most concerned her. He seemed to go from one health challenge to the next, making Iva happy he didn't resist turning things over to her. Now June and Inez were starting to deal with medical issues. *Ironic that after all my suffering and dysentery problems, I'm the healthiest in the family.*

Flipping through the pile of mail on her desk, Iva was pleased to discover Christmas cards from several of the matrons at Alderson including Warder Houchins. It was funny to now have such warm feelings for what should have been lost years, but Cousens' advice to learn from every day paid dividends.

At the bottom of the pile, she discovered a letter from Collins. Opening it quickly, she learned the latest application for a presidential pardon was dead, and another application could not be submitted immediately. When the timing was right, Collins would be in touch with how to proceed. Reading on, she caught her breath. DeWolfe had committed suicide in a Seattle hotel room. He left no note, so there was only speculation regarding a cause. More than one of DeWolfe's colleagues heard him speak of guilt as he had allowed his orders to prosecute Iva override his commitment to justice. Collins also noted that three of the female radio broadcasters who worked with Iva were recently granted US citizenship: Ruth Hayakawa, Miyeko Furiya Oki, and Katherine Moroka Reyes. The wife of a witness who testified against her was rewarded citizenship.

Iva leaned back and closed her eyes as images of these individuals flooded her mind. *I can still hear DeWolfe and his incessant objections that were solely intended to get in the way of my defense. Maybe in the end his conscience got the best of him, but as Collins wrote, that is only speculation. My coworkers getting US citizenship bothers me the most. They chose not to resist the authorities at the start of the war or renounce their loyalty to America. Now Miyeko Oki is being given citizenship. Her husband perjured himself and sent me to jail. Why was he not tried?*

A knock on the door brought her back to the present. "Iva, there's a supplier out back who needs to talk to you about his delivery."

She let the letter drop into the wastebasket. "Okay, I'm on my way."

IN 1968, THE JUSTICE DEPARTMENT NOTIFIED IVA THAT they were starting proceedings to collect the outstanding $10,000 fine. Collins issued a blistering press release in which he accused the US government of pursuing a strategy of harassment. He pointed out that most fines imposed by the government go uncollected, so when the Justice

Department decided to spend much more than $10,000 in personnel time and expenses to go after a penniless woman, what else could it be?

Still, the fine had to be dealt with. In the legal discovery process conducted by the Justice Department, Iva admitted that her father bought two small life insurance policies as investments for when she was older. The government demanded she cash them in, yielding $4,795. When pushed as to how she planned to pay the balance, Iva responded that she had no assets or means to pay. This led to arguments between Iva and her father. Jun wanted to cover the rest of the fine, but Iva insisted it was her debt. After a lot of back and forth, she wrung a promise from her father to agree to her wishes. Eventually, the Justice Department recognized the uselessness of chasing Iva and stopped bothering her.

That same year, Collins filed another presidential pardon application with President Lyndon Johnson in the last two months of his term. Her attorney told her, "The six-year window is open since the last application, so we might as well give it a try. If Johnson doesn't act during his lame duck days, maybe we can get Nixon's attention." Iva soon learned neither president would act.

Four years later, 1972 started with the news that the Japanese government would present Jun with an award for his service helping Japanese immigrants assimilate in America. Before he left, Jun asked, "Are you sorry, Daughter, you cannot come with me to Japan?"

"No, Dad. For once, I'm glad I don't have a passport. If you have time, I'd like you to try and see Mrs. Furuya and Mrs. Kido, two of my landladies. They did so much to help me."

"I will make a special trip to see them and thank them for taking care of my girl. How about Filipe? Do you want me to look him up?"

"No, Dad. Better to leave that alone."

Although Jun stated this honor was no big deal when he traveled to Japan, he discovered it was national news there. Numerous Japanese relatives reached out to congratulate him. Fortunately no one from the Hattori family was among that group. When he returned, Jun told Iva how angry he still was with how they had treated her.

SHORTLY AFTER JUN'S RETURN, IVA GOT A CALL FROM her brother. "Dad suffered a stroke an hour ago and was dead by the time he got to the hospital. I'm with him now."

Gathering her things and rushing out the door, Iva felt more crushed than at any time in Japan or during her trial. Already word was spreading among the significant Japanese American population in Chicago, and several representatives of that community waited in the hospital lobby.

Once in the hospital room, Iva hugged her brother and sisters and leaned down to give her father an embrace and kiss.

Fred said, "Dad had plans and money set aside for his funeral, so we have to follow his instructions." He paused. "So typical of Jun, Iva. There's something he asked me to share with you only after he passed. In his will, there's a provision to pay the rest of your debt to the government. He said he knows you didn't want him to do this, but when he meets Fumi in heaven, she would be angry with him if he hadn't paid the fine."

Iva looked down at her father and gave him a final hug. *Even in death, thinking of me.*

THE PERSON ON THE PHONE SAID, "HELLO, I'M TRYING to reach Iva Toguri D'Aquino." *Probably another one of the harassing calls that arrive periodically.* When getting ready to hang up, she heard, "If this is Mrs. D'Aquino, please give me a minute, since I'm calling with some positive news."

Iva said nothing but didn't put down the receiver.

The caller said, "Okay, silence there. I'm sure you get a lot of prank calls. My name is Dr. Clifford Uyeda, and I live in San Francisco. Since I retired, I've been doing work with the Japanese American Citizens League, and there's a developing sense among our members that you haven't been treated well by our organization."

Not treated well! That's the understatement of the year. Too scared for anyone to speak up during the trial. Wayne often ranted about how the JACL abandoned me.

"Mrs. D'Aquino, are you there?"

She said cautiously, "Yes, go on."

"Thank you. Last year I read a master's thesis by John Hada, a student at the University of San Francisco, about your indictment and trial. It's clear from his research that the charges against you were trumped up and the proceedings unfair. It opened my eyes. I read everything about your trial I could find. Hada and I approached the JACL to share what we learned. I have to say, Mrs. D'Aquino, that to the new generation of Japanese Americans who were children during the war, your story is a revelation and another example of our government discriminating against those of Japanese ancestry. The JACL encouraged me to form a committee to approach you."

After another pause, Iva asked, "What do you want?"

"We want to make amends, Mrs. D'Aquino. If you're willing to accept our apology, we can figure out the best way to deliver that. We have an annual dinner, and one option is to fly you out to San Francisco and state it publicly. If you have another way you'd like to handle that process, we're open to your wishes."

It's 1974, and the JACL is finally waking up to how they abandoned me. Now they want a dinner and a public event that will revive all the crackpots.

"Mrs. D'Aquino, it's quiet on your end again. What are your thoughts?"

"Thanks, but no thanks. I don't need any more publicity in my life. All I want is quiet and to be left alone. Thanks for calling."

She hung up. *Dad would probably want me to at least listen since he did so much work for Japanese Americans, but I don't need any more harassment.*

⌒

AFTER ANOTHER BUSY DAY, IVA SAT ALONE IN HER APARTment, rubbing her tired feet. Looking over at her new book, she relished a quiet hour of reading. There was a knock on the door. Who could it be? No one normally bothered her at this hour. Hopefully it wasn't a neighbor with some emergency. Dragging herself to her feet, she heard a more insistent knock.

"Okay, okay, I'm coming. Hold your horses."

Opening the door, Iva saw a tall Japanese man and several other Japanese behind him. "Mrs. D'Aquino, I'm Clifford Uyeda. We spoke briefly on the phone before we were cut off. Do you remember me?"

A wave of embarrassment hit Iva as she remembered hanging up. "Yes, I remember, and I'm sorry..."

"There's no need to apologize, Mrs. D'Aquino. You've been through a lot, and no one in our organization was there to support you. We took a chance to fly here and speak with you to show our sincerity. I have members of my committee behind me. We can make that apology now and leave you alone if that's what you wish, or we can explore a public apology. We're also sorry for being so rude as to show up unannounced and interrupt your day."

Iva was stunned. They had taken the chance to fly there because she hung up on Uyeda's call. Her eyes grew wet as she remembered Charles Cousens' advice not to be bitter about the past. She stammered, "I'm sorry. Your visit is such a surprise. Please come in. I don't have much space or enough chairs. I could make some tea. Have you eaten?"

"Mrs. D'Aquino, that's generous, and we don't want to impose. We noticed on our way that there's a small restaurant on the corner. It might be more comfortable for us to visit there."

A short time later, everyone was getting settled in a coffee shop. Uyeda introduced his delegation. "Again, we apologize for dropping in unannounced. We appreciate you're willing to meet with us."

As Iva heard several murmurs and comments of agreement, she choked up and started to cry. She tried to hide her tears in her hands as the men were silent. "It's been so hard," she said. "I was alone, and the politics made me a victim of the time. Even today, it doesn't stop. Whenever my name goes public, the media jumps on the story, and I start getting threats. I swear there are people out there who think I started the whole war. I'm tired of the need to hide."

Uyeda reached out and touched her arm. "None of us want to stir things up, so if it causes you pain, we can leave, but times are changing. We believe it's time to tell your story and educate people about the injustice you experienced and are still suffering. We talked to Wayne Collins before we came out here, and I have a letter from him." After reaching into his satchel, he handed a letter to Iva.

"I bet Wayne thinks I should work with you."

"Yes, he does. He thinks changing the narrative of your story will contribute to a presidential pardon."

Holding the unopened letter, Iva wiped her eyes. "All right. Just for the sake of argument, what do you gentlemen have in mind?"

CHAPTER 44

Not quite a year later, Iva found herself sitting with Uyeda and other committee members after an evening JACL awards dinner. The focus of the evening was to apologize formally and announce the awareness campaign that was about to kick off. Several times that day, she still found it hard to believe there actually was a plan to communicate her story methodically. The ultimate goal was to announce a new presidential pardon petition. This application would be filed after election day in 1976, so her case wouldn't be a campaign issue.

As the group discussed the next steps, Iva caught the eye of Wayne Collins Jr. The eleven-year-old boy she had tutored in algebra was now an attorney who everyone said was the spitting image of his dad. After his father's death on a recent flight from Hawaii, Wayne Jr. informed Iva that he would take over her case. As with his father, there would be no fee. Since Tamba had also recently passed away, without Wayne Jr., Iva knew she would be at a real disadvantage. For all the suffering and dishonesty Iva had experienced over the years, tonight she felt like she was surrounded by people who truly had her best interests at heart.

Uyeda said, "We're agreed. Step one is to finalize and publish a pamphlet titled Victim of a Legend. The release will be early next year and sent to every major newspaper in the country. We'll all have responsibilities at that time to follow up with key press members and politicians. Our communication strategy will have to be flexible as we gauge results and whether there are any groups we especially need to address."

"The Veterans of Foreign Wars is an especially conservative organization and likely to oppose," Wayne Jr. said.

"Good point, Wayne. That's why I have them on my list to contact. I doubt we can get them turned around, but I'll give it my best shot. All this will lead up to an application going to the president right after the election. If somehow that peanut farmer from Georgia beats Ford, then as a lame duck, the president may be free of longer-term political concerns. Since Ford will likely win, we'll have to deal with politics at that time. Wayne, you said you'd draft the application for a pardon, right?"

"Got it."

"Well, I think that should wrap it up for the night. The dinner went well, and it's clear our members are behind this campaign. Iva, any last thoughts?"

Leaning forward, she said, "All I can say is thanks to everyone for all you're doing. When some of you showed up a year ago in Chicago, I wanted you to go away. For the first time in years, I have hope this may turn out positively. If my dad were here, he'd also want to thank you."

ONCE THE CAMPAIGN WAS UNDERWAY, IVA WAS AMAZED at how fast it progressed and the positive results. After the release of the pamphlet describing Iva's trial, Ronald Yates, the Far East correspondent for the *Chicago Tribune*, wrote a series of articles outlining the injustice that occurred during her trial. The bombshell at the center of the two-part series was the quotes from Mitsushio and Oki admitting that the FBI had threatened them and forced their perjured statements. Yates wrote that both witnesses stated, "We had no choice. The US occupation police came and said we must testify against Iva or else. In San Francisco, along with other government witnesses, we were drilled with what to say and not to say by the FBI for two hours every morning weeks before the trial started. If we didn't cooperate, Uncle Sam would arrange a trial for us."

On the morning of Yates' first story, the Toguri Mercantile Store was besieged by press members wanting statements. Iva struggled with how to react and decided to ask a local television newsman for help. Bill Kurtis, who had known Iva's family for several years, told her to keep the press outside. He was on the way.

When he was sequestered behind her closed office door, Kurtis said, "I've contacted New York, and they reached a preliminary agreement to get you on the news tonight with Walter Cronkite. Walter's very fair, and by doing his broadcast, you'll reach the greatest audience and present your story through the most respected newsman in the country."

"I can't believe *CBS News* would want to talk to me. You said preliminary approval. What if they decide not to do it?"

"Don't worry. Cronkite will want the story. That means we've got a few hours to go over what you want to say and what he'll ask you."

"What about the press outside the store right now?"

"Leave them there. If nothing else, it's good advertising for your store."

⌒

THE INTERVIEW WITH WALTER CRONKITE WENT WELL. The nation saw a small, sixty-year-old woman telling how she was railroaded by the FBI and the US Justice Department. In the current era of Watergate and protests against the Vietnam War, the suspicion that the government could be dishonest was timely. Soon reporters from around the country were picking up her story and uncovering additional transgressions during her trial. That was followed by local governments passing numerous resolutions supporting clemency. None was more significant than the Los Angeles City Council, which rescinded its resolution from 1948 opposing Iva's return to the United States.

Three months later, Iva, her family members, and Kurtis sat down to watch that Sunday's broadcast of *60 Minutes* and her interview with Morley Safer. As the story wrapped up, Safer said, "This year, a pardon application is being filed on her behalf. A presidential pardon, we remind you, does not bestow innocence on the pardoned person, nor can it restore the fine or the years spent in prison. In Iva's case, it would give back something of great value to her: the full rights of her American citizenship."

The room erupted with hugs and congratulations. Kurtis was especially jubilant. "Everyone knows Ford never misses *60 Minutes*. That was the best way to get your story in front of him."

Standing on the corner of Seventh and Mission Streets in San Francisco on a chilly November 17, memories filled Iva's mind. This was the location of the former federal courthouse where the trial took place. Wayne Jr. picked this location for the news conference to remind everyone of the trial. Now that Iva was national news, she was still surprised at the number of press people who showed up on occasions like this. Since Jimmy Carter beat Gerald Ford in the recent election, everyone agreed her chances for a pardon would be higher with the lame duck president.

The event started with Wayne Jr. talking about the work of his father, the defense team, and previous presidential pardon efforts. He explained that with the recently recanted testimony and apologies from many of the witnesses who spoke against Iva, this pardon was never more deserved. Indicating the application would be forwarded to the White House that day, he called upon the president to take swift action.

Iva made a brief statement, thanking everyone for putting the petition together and adding that she'd never done anything treasonous and had always been loyal to the United States. "I was never Tokyo Rose. There was no Tokyo Rose. A lot of things happened, and I was in the wrong place at the wrong time."

A member of the press called out, "Iva, what about resistance from some groups like the Veterans of Foreign Wars to your application?"

"Let me take that one," Wayne Jr. said as he took the microphone. "We've spoken with the VFW and believe their opposition is unfortunate. Many still feel the pain from the years of war. We believe over time groups such as the VFW will come to realize the injustice served upon this innocent woman."

"Follow-up question, Wayne. What about the survey by the *Detroit Free Press* that said 72 percent of their readers oppose clemency for Iva?"

"I don't know how that poll was conducted, but when you look nationally, we see nothing but support for justice that's been long denied. I believe that continued education will bring more people around."

As Collins continued to parry with the press, Iva felt the wind give her a chill. *This application is still not a sure thing. What if Ford chooses to leave office without taking any action? This application is my last chance to get a pardon and my full citizenship back.*

———

Two weeks later, on a Saturday, Iva answered a knock on the door of her apartment and saw two tall FBI agents holding up their credentials and asking if she had a few minutes to answer some questions. A sense of dread flooded her as she flashed back to previous interactions with the FBI. Seeing her hesitation and concern, one agent said, "We're doing the necessary background check for a presidential pardon. Our questions should be brief and shouldn't create a difficult situation for you."

Breathing a sigh of relief, Iva said, "Come in, as long as Agent Tillman is not with you."

Knowing who Tillman was and the role he played in her case, the agent said, "Tillman is long gone from the agency, I assure you."

CHAPTER 45

The waiting game was on. Iva tried not to get too hopeful about the pardon. After all she had been through, it was difficult to not think many times a day about the status of her application. She talked with many people about their interactions with the FBI as part of the vetting process. While everyone was optimistic, Wayne Jr. cautioned her that it wasn't complete until the president acted.

One difference with this application was the involvement of Senator S. I. Hayakawa of California. A colleague and friend of President Ford, Hayakawa lobbied the president personally about the pardon. Iva warmly remembered the first time the senator telephoned to say he would lean on President Ford to take the deserved action.

"You know, Iva, I owe a lot to your family," Hayakawa said.

"What might that be?"

"Your father worked to help many Japanese nationals struggling to get into the United States even though citizenship was prohibited. Like your pop, my dad traveled through Canada to get around the system. On one trip, my father brought his new bride from Japan just like Jun brought your mother, Fumi. My mother was pregnant. The Canadian authorities said her paperwork wasn't in order, and she'd have to return immediately to Japan rather than travel on to the United States, which meant she'd likely give birth on the ship back to Japan. Your father intervened, and with his connections, he got the paperwork straightened out. Her child was born in Canada. That baby was me."

Tears streamed down Iva's face. *You've done it again, Dad. Looking out for me after all these years. I'll have to bring extra flowers this week when I visit your grave.*

RUMORS WERE THAT THE PARDON MIGHT BE ISSUED ON Christmas Day, but there was no word on that holiday. On January 3, Uyeda sent a telegram to President Ford saying the announcement of the pardon at the Wayne Collins Sr. Appreciation Dinner scheduled for January 8 would be auspicious, but that date came and went. With the inauguration of Jimmy Carter scheduled for January 20, Iva became more convinced it wasn't going to happen with each day that passed. She dragged herself through her workdays, attempting to put the process out of her mind.

On the morning of January 20, Iva noticed members of the press starting to filter into the store. Her heart started to race when one of her clerks came up and said, "Bill Kurtis just slipped in the back door and wants to see you in your office."

Rushing upstairs and closing the door behind her, she saw Kurtis' big grin as he stepped forward and embraced her. "The pardon came through. Congratulations."

As she stepped back, struggling with her emotions, she said, "Are you sure? Is it real?"

"Cliff is on the phone, and he has a direct line open to

the White House attorney working on this. Talk to them and ask for yourself."

Iva picked up the phone with a shaking hand. "Cliff, is it true?"

"Iva, I have the White House attorney here. He can tell you directly what the president did this morning."

"Mrs. D'Aquino, I'm the attorney assigned to this case. Just before leaving the Oval Office for the last time, President Ford signed a pardon for you. We're preparing the paperwork right now and will overnight the documentation to you. Congratulations, Mrs. D'Aquino."

Iva handed the phone to Kurtis and fell into her chair. June, who had quietly slipped in, leaned over to hug her sister as the women wept.

It's over. I'm a full American citizen again. We did it, Dad, and I couldn't have gotten my citizenship back without you.

Epilogue

IN 1980, FILIPE PURSUED A DIVORCE THAT IVA DIDN'T CON-
test. He passed away in 1998 while still in Japan.
Iva Toguri died of a stroke on September 26, 2006.
In the days following the presidential pardon, she lived a
quiet life managing the Toguri Mercantile Company of Chicago and experiencing the peaceful existence she longed for.
With the change in public perception about her involvement
in broadcasting for Radio Tokyo, much of the harassment
and hate disappeared, allowing her to travel. Over the years,
some of her trips became annual events to visit several of
the guards she had grown close to while in West Virginia.
Those relationships exemplified the positive impact Iva had
on others no matter how events kept working against her.

A Note from the Author

ALL THE EVENTS AND PEOPLE CITED ARE REAL. AT TIMES I may have slightly changed a timeline for the sake of the narrative. The dialogue represents what might have occurred, although occasionally I use an exact quote if available. Numerous books and articles have been written about Iva Toguri and her life, and I stand in awe of those comprehensive and insightful studies. In writing this book, any criticism of how I portrayed events must fall only on me.

Attempting to understand what happened to this woman should inform us about current and future abuses of power that could affect any of us. One maxim in the study of history is that we are condemned to repeat our past. Iva was a convenient target when Attorney General Tom Clark decided President Truman needed to look tough on treason during the 1948 election. Innocent and well-intentioned people are similarly victimized today, given the current era of extreme politics.

There is no doubt about the existence of racism in our society. The blatant actions taken against Japanese Americans before and during World War II are an especially dark chapter. Iva faced that prejudice in her early years when she was denied entrance to medical school and later as a loyal American in Japan when she refused to change citizenship.

The US government leveraged society's racism by making sure Iva's trial was in San Francisco, a city with a history of anti-Japanese sentiment. Iva and the defense team drew Judge Michael Roche, who was biased from the start of the trial. Following the trial, Judge Roche was documented as stating he suspected from the start that Iva was a willing participant in treason. The judge's perception ignored the other events during her years in Japan.

Being a single woman trapped in the militaristic society of Japan put her at another serious disadvantage. Under a system where food was used to control people, Iva could not get the basic staples granted to those around her. Her creativity in smuggling needed food and medicines to American POWs goes beyond what most would have been able to accomplish. Through those years in Japan, her courage and self-sacrifice were heroic.

It is noteworthy that the male radio announcers, who typically had the lead in reading the news for Radio Tokyo, were never tried for treason. George Mitsushio and Ken-kichi Oki, Iva's managers, both were born in the United States. In Japan, they exercised their right to Japanese citizenship through the Family Registry. Neither formally renounced their American citizenship. If anyone deserved to be tried for treason as US citizens who fully embraced the Japanese war effort, it was these two men. Instead, Mitsushio and Oki agreed to commit perjury to avoid prosecution and were rewarded with the full privileges of American citizenship. The excesses of the FBI and Justice Department should serve as a warning for all Americans about the ease with which our liberties can be sacrificed when fear rules politics.

The final question that dominated my research was whether Iva was guilty of treason at some level. My conclusion is that technically she was guilty of reading those critical words about American ships being lost after the Battle of Leyte Gulf. By the time of the broadcast, Charles Cousens and Ted Ince were no longer there to protect her, and the Japanese army's increasing insistence to get more hard-hitting propaganda in the *Zero Hour* broadcasts left Iva with little choice but to read the scripts put in front of her. However, the historical impact of these words was minimal in the grand scheme of things. The American victory at Leyte Gulf was decisive and completed almost a month before her fateful broadcast. While the Americans lost a few ships, the damage imposed by the Americans in that battle essentially ended the Japanese navy's fighting capability.

What would any of us have done in her shoes? Those few words she read gave the US government an opening, but when compared to the larger picture of how Iva conducted herself in Japan, there was no justice in her fate. After sentencing, more than one juror, including the foreman, publicly admitted being worn down by the others who wanted the deliberations expedited.

Iva Toguri was a strong, courageous woman who made mistakes along the way but never gave up on life. She stated more than once that she believed her life was destined for hardship, and if she were not trapped in Japan, some other misfortune would have come her way. For a woman who believed in and longed to live the American dream, the government of her beloved country denied her that opportunity for much of her life.

Acknowledgements

THERE ARE MANY PEOPLE TO THANK FOR THEIR HELP AND support along the way. First, Terry Esvelt, who told me as I contemplated retirement that I would write a book in the ensuing years. I scoffed, but because of his encouragement, here I am. His reviews of my work always result in strategic course corrections. My first editor, Jill Kelley, has been someone who pushes in just the right way. The progress I've made as a writer has been under her steady hand. Support and critical reviews came from early readers including Carole Ambroziak, Leri Ferreira, Shirley Henderson, Bruce Kirshner, Karen Meadows, and Mark Rothert. Special thanks to Bill Kurtis, who was gracious with his reviews since he played such a critical role in Iva's life. Frederick Close, author of a definitive history of Iva's life in *Tokyo Rose: An American Patriot*, was generous in sharing resources. The people at Luminare Press have been nothing short of terrific. My gratitude to Kim Harper-Kennedy, Jamie Passaro, Melissa Thomas, Patricia Marshall, and Lori Stephens. Finally, thanks to my most important reviewer and critic, Sue Weedall, who inspires me every day with her love.

Additional Information

Charles River Editors. *Tokyo Rose: The History and Legacy of Iva Toguri and Japan's Most Famous Propaganda Campaign During World War II.*

Close, Frederick P. *Tokyo Rose: An American Patriot: A Dual Biography.* Lanham, MD: Rowman & Littlefield Publishers, 2014.

Duss, Masayo. *Tokyo Rose, Orphan of the Pacific.* New York: Harper & Row, 1979.

Federal Bureau of Investigation. http://www.fbi.gov/about-us/history/famous-cases/tokyo-rose.

Federal Communications Commission. "Zero Hour, August 14, 1944 (Tokyo Rose)." https://archive.org/details/ZeroHour08141944.

Gunn, Rex B. *They Called Her Tokyo Rose.* Japanese American Citizens League, 1977.

Hada, John. *The Indictment and Trial of Iva Ikuko Toguri d'Aquino—Tokyo Rose.* Masters Thesis, University of San Francisco, September 1949.

Howe, Russel Warren. *The Hunt for Tokyo Rose.* Lanham, MD: Madison Books, 1990.

Japanese American Citizens League. "Iva Toguri d'Aquino: Victim of a Legend." San Francisco, National Committee for Iva Toguri, November 1976.

Kawashima, Yasuhide. *The Tokyo Rose Case: Treason on Trial.* Lawrence, KS: University Press of Kansas, 1990.

Minear, Richard H., ed. *The Scars of War: Tokyo During World War II.* Lanham, MD: Rowman and Littlefield, 2007.

Yamashita, Samuel Hideo. *Daily Life in Wartime Japan, 1940–1945.* Lawrence, KS: University Press of Kansas, 2015.

YouTube. "Sixty Minutes: Iva Toguri." 1976. https://www.youtube.com/watch?v=1rEEk6JP9vc&t=948s.

Zero Hour Broadcasts. http://www.earthstation1.com/TheZeroHour.html.